POETRY MATTERS

Edited by Claire Tupholme

Northern Ireland, Scotland & Wales

First published in Great Britain in 2011 by:

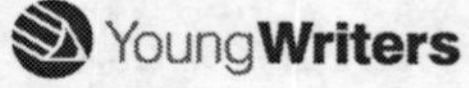

Remus House
Coltsfoot Drive
Peterborough
PE2 9BF
Telephone: 01733 890066
Website: www.youngwriters.co.uk

Book Design by Tim Christian

SB ISBN 978-0-85739-522-1

Foreword

Since our inception in 1991, Young Writers has endeavoured to promote poetry and creative writing within schools by running annual nationwide competitions. These competitions are designed to develop and nurture the burgeoning creativity of the next generation, and give them valuable confidence in their own abilities.

This regional anthology is one of the series produced by our latest secondary school competition, *Poetry Matters*. Using poetry as their tool, the young writers were given the opportunity to tell the world what matters to them. The authors of our favourite three poems were also given the chance to appear on the front cover of their region's collection.

Whilst skilfully conveying their opinions through poetry, the writers showcased in this collection have simultaneously managed to give poetry a breath of fresh air, brought it to life and made it relevant to them. Using a variety of themes and styles, our featured poets leave a lasting impression of their inner thoughts and feelings, making this anthology a rare insight into the next generation.

Contents

St Richard Gwyn Catholic High School, Barry

Sanquhar Academy, Broomfield

Stobhill School, Glasgow

Taibah School, Cardiff

Ysgol Gyfun Gwynllyw, Pontypool

Ysgol Plas Brondyffryn, Denbigh

Ysgol-Y-Gwendraeth, Llanelli

The Poems

My Life At Beechwood

When I arrived at Beechwood I wasn't very shy
But it definitely will be hard for me to say goodbye.

I love to eat rice
And the staff at Beechwood are extremely nice.

Beechwood will always be there for me
And I will always make their tea.

One day my cupboards were bare
And my favourite member of staff is Claire.

Beechwood staff are loving and caring
And they are always ready and raring.

Natasha (18)

Wonderful Wildlife

Up high in the canopies,
Or down by the seven seas,
A corruptness is taking place
And at an alarming pace.

Lives are being disrupted,
Creatures are interrupted,
Wildlife is put on hold,
As properties are sold.

Animals are put in fear
As machines start to appear.
And the workers' only concern
Is how much salary they earn.

Who wants to see litter anyway?
It's always nature that has to pay.
Daffodils wilt and animals die,
Streams are polluted, smog in the sky.

Humans are home-hacking and tree-trashing,
Workers are love-lacking and nest-gnashing,
Forests are made so hideous and bare,
Animals leave, no sanctuary there.

The countryside, once so beautiful,
The rainforests were so colourful,
Set in the sun and air,
Wildlife always thrives there.

But not anymore,
We just can't ignore,
The injustice going on,
On the Earth we live upon.

It isn't fair, it isn't right,
It's hardly an appealing sight,
It's disgusting through and through,
Think, what has the world come to?

So take action and conserve,
Protect, defend and preserve!
Try and help our four-legged friends,
Until this indecency ends!

So leave the brambles and the trees,
The tigers, the fish, birds and bees
So fight with those in the strife
Save our wonderful wildlife!

Catherine Gibson (14)
Aquinas Grammar School, Belfast

Welsh Prince, Oh Welsh Prince

Welsh prince, oh welsh prince
The rinse of your blades,
The lads who follow you great princes to the grave.
May our modern government take note of your greatness
And rate of your hearts
Oh great prince may your praises be sung
In bands of merry Welshmen.

Rhys Larsen (17)
Beechwood College, Sully

Elly

Excellent Elly sat on the telly
Lovely playing the games away
Lounging around all day
Yes, doing it the lazy way!

Elly Brown (21)
Beechwood College, Sully

Past And Present Collide

I awoke one night to see a cage,
There was a boy inside the cage.
I asked the boy, 'Why the cage?'
He said, 'It's safe.'
The boy seemed familiar
So I looked closer.
The boy was shaking and crying,
I asked the boy, 'Why the tears?'
He said, 'They hurt.'
I asked, 'What hurt?'
'The schools,' he said.
The cage just disappeared as if it was never there.
I hugged the boy and in a gentle voice I said,
'You're me, aren't you?'
The boy replied, 'You took your time to realise.'

David Telling (18)
Beechwood College, Sully

Holidays

My parents go on holiday
To wherever they like to stay
They have been lots of times.

They always have fun wherever they go
I thought you would like to know
They always enjoy themselves
They stay in a place, they really like it
And maybe they stay in a deep pit.

They always go to the water park
When it is very dark
They go on the waterslides
And then on the rides.

When they go to exciting places
They never tie up their shoelaces
They always forget.

When they are all wet
They look for a house to let
If they can afford it
They go to the seaside
And they always hide.

My parents enjoy their holidays
In a lot of ways.

Kristina Evans (21)
Beechwood College, Sully

Remember

Remember when you lived in fear?
Remember when I wasn't here?
Remember when it started?
Remember when the couples parted?
Remember when the world went to war?
Remember when I didn't turn up at the door?
Remember when that telegram came?
Remember when you felt that terrible pain?
Remember when people asked?
Remember when you changed the subject fast?
Remember when you cried at night?
Remember when you saw the sight?
Remember when I died?
Remember when you wanted to hide?
Remember when I told you I wanted to fight?
Remember when I said it would be alright?
Remember when you tucked me into bed?
Remember when you brought me Ted?
Remember when I went to school?
Remember when I thought war would be cool?
Remember when you remember me?
Remember when you picture me as a busy bee?
Remember when I was born?
Remember when your heart got torn?
Remember when I said I loved you?
Remember when you replied, 'I love you too'?
Remember when we all had fun?
Remember when work had to be done?
Remember when I got a girlfriend?
Remember when I wore the latest trend?
Remember when I grew up?
Remember when your world blew up?
Remember I love you
That's the one thing that will always be true.

Ceri Anne Brown (13)
Bryn Hafren Comprehensive School, Barry

Earth Matters To Me

Earth matters to me for a lot of different reasons
Like the way it changes throughout the different seasons
Different species of animals live among us here
But sadly because of us, some of them will disappear

The plants here are amazing, too good to be true
But again because of us, they'll disappear too
Earth is our home and we're destroying it any way we can
With things such as pollution and deforestation

This planet matters to me because it's my home you know
But if we kill it, the big question is where do we go?
So changing the way we live, the now, might help Earth's future too
That's what really matters to me is making sure that we do.

Keira McLean (14)
Calderhead High School, Shotts

Squirrels

S ee squirrels up your tree
Q uivering excitedly
U se binoculars to see
I t feasting on his nuts
R usty coloured squirrels
R ace from branch to branch
E ager for the summer
L ively enjoying a dance.

Paris Melton (11)
Connah's Quay High School, Connah's Quay

Shooter's Story

You're bright red in the face
You're feeling bad
Only three minutes left to play
Being cheered on by your dad.

Dodge over here
Looking for the ball
Jump! You got it! Pass it quick!
Get in a space, shout and call!

You have the ball,
It's all up to you
You lift it up high
This is your cue.

The crowd go silent
You feel the strain
You feel the pressure
No pain, no gain.

The ball goes up
The ball goes in
The whistle blows
Another great win.

Molly Edwards (11)
Connah's Quay High School, Connah's Quay

My School Lunch

A candy bar
A packet of crisps
A hot dog
And a few chips - *yum!*
A jelly cube
A stick candy
A sherbert tube
And a can of shandy.

A Wagon Wheel
Some bubblegum
A banana peel
And a bit of rum.
Some chocolate fingers
And Party Rings
That's all I'm allowed to bring.

My mum slept in,
Well, I made my lunch!

Caitlin Smith (12)
Connah's Quay High School, Connah's Quay

Monster Town

Monster number 5 is slimy and green,
He is the strangest thing you have ever seen.

Monster number 4 is spotty and pink,
Snails and slugs are what he likes to drink.

Monster number 3 is small and thin,
He could fit into a ravioli tin.

Monster number 2 is spiny and round,
He is as fast as a greyhound.

Monster number 1 looks like a clown,
These are the 5 most dangerous monsters in Monster Town.

Millie Williams (11)
Connah's Quay High School, Connah's Quay

The Tiger

Fast runner
What a stunner!

Deadly scratcher
Animal catcher.

Strong fighter
Great biter.

Such a killer
What a thriller.

Winning racer
Great chaser.

Not a hiker
But a striker
One big tiger!

Megan Price (11)
Connah's Quay High School, Connah's Quay

The Colours Of My Feelings

Green is the colour of happiness,
The colour of plants and leaves mean springtime is here,
I think of happy days to come.

Blue is the colour of calmness,
The colour of tranquil waters lapping at the shore,
It makes me feel relaxed inside.

Yellow is the colour of hunger,
The colour of my rumbling stomach before teatime,
I think of cheese and bananas.

Red is the colour of romance,
The colour of the heart that beats inside everyone,
I think of my true love.

Orange is the colour of optimism,
The colour of the paint I used to paint my ginger locks,
I think about what they say about me but I don't care.

Grey is the colour of sadness,
The colour of the clouds on a story day,
I think about all the people I loved that have died.

Black is the colour of anger,
The colour of the storm cloud that drifts over my head,
I think about how much I want to hurt those people.

Pink is the colour of joy,
The colour of the words that float through my mind,
I think of a sunny day when we all go out to play.

White is the colour of loneliness,
The colour of the room I stand alone in,
I think of all the people that leave me.

Molly Gregorious (12)
Connah's Quay High School, Connah's Quay

A Haunted House

It was raining outside
Thunder and lightning
The car had stopped
It was so, so frightening.

I got out of the car
And spotted a toad
I followed it up
A long winding road.

The rain was pelting
The wind was blowing
I looked ahead
To see a light glowing.

At the top of the hill
Stood a house, so creepy
I felt so afraid
I started to get weepy.

I walked to the house
I pushed open the door
There were creaking noises
I was scared even more.

I walked up the stairs
And saw a shape
A man ran past
In a hat and a cape.

It all goes black
I let out a scream
I open my eyes . . .
It's all just a dream!

Ellie Humphreys (11)
Connah's Quay High School, Connah's Quay

Jelly Beans

First of all bean number one
Butterscotch is lots of fun
Keep number two away from Mum
It's time to hide some bubblegum
Next up is marshmallow
This makes me a happy fellow
Lemon and lime is number four
This jelly bean ends up on the floor
The yellow bean is popcorn
Whoever eats it will be reborn
Raspberry is jelly six
I found it in a pick 'n' mix
Let me tell you about tangy tangerine
Trust me it tastes of Listerine
If English blackberry you do pick
The likelihood you will be sick
South sea kiwi is number nine
OMG this tastes divine
The black one is liquorice
I don't think it tastes delish
Number eleven is tropical mango
After I ate I danced the tango
Cranberry and apple is rather nice
The texture is like melting ice
Which jelly rhymes with Daily Planet?
Oh I know, it's pomegranate
Banana split is number fourteen
My dad says it tastes pristine
Number fifteen is not fair
This bean tasted of sour pear
The dark brown bean is café latte
It goes well with a slice of pate
The strangest of them all is zingy lemon
'Cause this one smells of watermelon
Light and fluffy candyfloss
It makes your tongue say, 'I'm the boss!'
The most famous of them all is Coca-Cola
It's much more popular than gorgonzola

My mum's favourite is tropical punch
She will eat sixty of them for her lunch
A really nice one is blueberry pie
It's so great it makes me cry
The strongest bean is mint sorbet
I could eat it every day
Coconut is chewy and white
I dream of it all through the night
There is a smelly bean
The cheese jelly is extremely mean
Pina colada looks like a peanut
It is stored in a Caribbean hut
My favourite is number twenty-seven
It is a bite of chocolate Heaven.

Hope Cookson (12)
Connah's Quay High School, Connah's Quay

There's A Figure

There's a figure in my room
And it's creeping me out.

There's a figure in my room
And that's no doubt.

It's getting closer
But I can't see
It's breathing on my neck
And it's coming closer to me.

It's getting even closer
And I don't know what to do
You better be careful because
It might creep up on you!

You'll never guess what I saw
Last night, I saw a figure
And it gave me a fright.

I'm very scared about this haunting
Because it is so daunting.

I'm lying in bed with my body shaking in fear
Oh dear, the ghost is here!
Argh!

Amy Jane Gould (12)
Connah's Quay High School, Connah's Quay

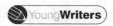

It's Not Fair

Why is grass green
Why don't snakes have hair?
Why is my sister mean?
Oh, it's not fair!

Why are my eyes brown?
Why are whales now rare?
Why do fish never frown?
Oh, it's not fair!

Why do I always come last?
Why is my dad's head bare?
Why am I not very fast?
Oh it's not fair!

Why are there shows about grime?
Why do bees always buzz?
Why doesn't this bit rhyme?
Oh wait, it does,
Now that's what I call fair!

Hannah Figoni (12)
Connah's Quay High School, Connah's Quay

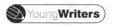

The Ballad Of Joanna Yeates

Joanna Yeates had gone drinking
Down to the pub with some friends
As she headed home thinking
I think I'll have pizza for tea.

But bad luck was to follow
As a visitor called that night
Someone had heard a holler
And Joanna was nowhere in sight.

The papers reported her missing
Her parents and boyfriend they wept
They cried, worried and keep on wishing
They'd catch him who Joanna kept.

Her body was sadly found
By an old couple on Christmas Day
Abandoned, alone on the frozen ground
Her young life stolen away.

Now a murder hunt has started
Her landlord looks guilty as sin
Is this the man who has parted
Joanna from her kith and her kin.

Jordan Hunter (12)
Connah's Quay High School, Connah's Quay

Excuse Poem

I tried to do my homework
But I figured I couldn't do it
So I chucked it in the bin
And thought, oh screw it.

I know the poem was a competition
And I thought I wouldn't win
So all the drafts I done
I put them in the bin.

Again I tried to do my homework
But the dog chewed it up
I put the rest in the bin
And then I gave it up.

I tried and tried and tired
But nothing pleases you
So I thought I'd write this poem
And I hope this will do.

Molly Amos (14)
Connah's Quay High School, Connah's Quay

I Swore

I just swore like the rest
To the badge on my chest
To the gun in my hand
I will fight for my land
In the cold, sweat and tears
When over all the years
You just weep bitter tears
Your friends lie in this mud
Just drowning in their blood.

Neil MacLean (13)
Culloden Academy, Inverness

My Own Ballad!

Down the stairs the family come
It's 8am, all they want is food
Everyone is in a hurry looking out their jotters
They're tired and in a bad mood.

Off to school and work they go
Walking and driving in the snow
All wrapped up from head to toe.

Everyone arrives in time, thank goodness
Maths, science, modern studies and French
I go to all these classes then it's lunch.

Walking home with my friends we chat as we walk,
It's dark, I am glad to get home
When I walk in the door I hear a dog barking.

Mollie Lisle (12)
Culloden Academy, Inverness

Dead And Gone

It was early in the month of May when Jane got the news
The news that her dear love John was now all gone
After perishing in the blues.

Distraught was this pretty girl, ran into her garden fine
So upset was she that she hung herself on a vine!

Her father found his daughter hanging from the vine
Swinging in a light little breeze beside the river's line.

Her father fell to his knees and cried out in pain
For his dear daughter Jane
He screamed that his daughter's life should not have been in vain.

Katie Macdonald (12)
Culloden Academy, Inverness

The Choice

A woman was in love
And his name was Jack
But little did she know
His heart was black.

As she loved another man it was time to choose
But where to start?
She never knew to go with
Her head or her heart.

'I'm sorry Jack but it had to be done
From now on you are not the man I choose
Yes, yes, it seems unfair
But I'm sorry Jack you lose.'

'My name is Jack and my heart is black
That couple will soon be dead
After that I shall go for a walk
And clear my busy head.'

When Jack entered the woman's house
The couple would soon die
As he fled the country
Together the couple would lie.

Kira Horne (13)
Culloden Academy, Inverness

War Veteran

I am scared by war
I am lucky, others are not
I wait my time.

I am scared by war
Remembering the old days gone
I still wait my time.

I am scared by war
My suffering is at an end
It's now my time.

Ryan Mackenzie (13)
Culloden Academy, Inverness

My Ballad

The family sat in the living room
In the comfy chairs
When suddenly the telly broke
But David shrugged, 'Who cares!'

Dad began to get angry and shouted,
'Get out, get out!
And if you don't this instant
I will give you a clout!'

David looked in horror
At the nuisance he had caused
It was just like the movie
In rewind or pause.

But David's dad forgave him
If he did some chores
Now they are all happy
Because peace reigns indoors.

David Oman (12)
Culloden Academy, Inverness

Ron And The Beast

There was a man called Ron
He was stuck in the 1950s
He was pretty scared
But it was pretty nifty.

He saw a lady with beautiful blonde hair
A big horrible beast came over
Ron was shocked at this
He needed the luck of a four leaf clover.

Ron needed to think quickly
The beautiful blonde was in danger
Ron wasn't made to fight
He wasn't exactly an army ranger.

He finally thought of what to do
He grabbed a knife in sheer fear
He pierced the beast in the stomach
He's just glad he can now have a beer.

He woke up from that horrible dream
He smiled with a sense of greatness
He got out of bed and looked at the time
Oh, oh, he better get to work or he will be punished for lateness.

After work he saw another beautiful blonde
He went over and said, 'Would you like a drink?'
She accepted with a smile on her face
How did it go? What do you think?

They had a beautiful wedding
In a beautiful church
Him and the blonde lived happily ever after
Then they decided to live in the beautiful Morayfirth.

Joe Farquhar (14)
Culloden Academy, Inverness

That Girl!

Two boys walked along the beach
Along the sunny bay
They saw a really pretty girl
This truly made their day!

When they saw her Ben raced ahead
And breathlessly asked her out
Fraser said he would ask her out
He thought she would say yes without a doubt!

'No thank you, I won't have you Ben,
And Fraser, not you either.'
So she walked away choosing neither!

Nicole Mullen (12)
Culloden Academy, Inverness

My Ballad

In Scotland, Inverness
A fight was going on
It was a right mess.

There was a man
A man called Will
That man was in that fight
He was on a hill.

There was a man
A man called Harry
He was waiting
With his brother Gary.

The battle started
Nobody was close to the win
Then they pierced each other's bodies
And they were dumped in a bin.

Connor Bain (12)
Culloden Academy, Inverness

Heart And Apart

Back in those December days
When everything was looking grey
A lady walked in the park and met a man
And for them it was a great day!

It was love at first sight
She stole the man's heart
They understood everything about each other
They never wanted to be apart!

They were sitting on the beach one day
When they broke out into a fight
The lady pushed the man into the water
And said, 'That serves you right!'

When that saga ended
They broke out with laughter
And do you know what happened next
They lived happily ever after!

Caitlan Sleet (12)
Culloden Academy, Inverness

War Veteran

W ar veterans
A re brave and proud
R emembering lost comrades

V ictorious in battle
E nemies are defeated
T ime on time again
E very man has had his day
R etired, respectable
A soldier so brave
N ever again.

David Caulfield (13)
Culloden Academy, Inverness

My Ballad

One summer day two girls were walking
They spied a man with his dog
As they walked over to the man he fell over a log.

'Excuse me Sir, may I help you?'
'Yes please,' said the man. 'Would you move this log?'
The girls moved it over and helped him get up
'Why thank you, would you lift up my dog?'

The second girl walked to the man
'Excuse me, you better choose me!'
'Actually I will not choose any
For I have to get home for my tea.

I'm sorry girls, I will have neither'
'But Sir, we were going to ask you out for dinner.
It'll be fun, the three of us'
'That's okay, for it will not help me get any thinner!'

Rhian Nestor (12)
Culloden Academy, Inverness

Down In Egypt

Down south in Egypt
There is a civil war
Civilians don't want the president
To rule their world anymore.

The people want him to resign
But all he does is refuse
All his colleagues have left him already
He thinks he cannot lose.

All his people are raging
Wrecking all the cities
Burning buildings, toppling cars
Soon Egypt will be in wee bitties.

Jordan Anderson (13)
Culloden Academy, Inverness

Together, Forever And Always

Back in those summer days
When everything was very bright
A lady took a stroll in the park and met a man
And for them it was a fantastic day.

It was love at first sight
She stole the man's soul
They knew each other inside out
They wanted to be together forever and always.

They were lying on the grass one night
Looking at the stars
They looked into each other's eyes
And she began to cry.

They were so in love
They said they would stay together forever
But if they did part
They wanted to die in each other's arms.

Jodie Clark (12)
Culloden Academy, Inverness

The Veteran

A veteran with a story
Explains the tragedy
Lights of guns shone like burning sun
Shouts were heard, urgent, bold, stick as one!

No one wanted the dreadful job
To knock on doors, leave people robbed
Muted shock in true disbelief
'I'm sorry . . . your son is dead,' said the chief.

I return home a lucky man
For some a back to normality plan
For others it was just the start
Travelling back to the halfway mark.

Sarah Stuart (13)
Culloden Academy, Inverness

Outstanding Veterans!

Veterans who stand tall and proud
And like to hear their voices loud.
Went to war, came back with scars,
To commemorate their life so far.

They're coming home but some shall stay
The ones that are home went all the way.
They proudly walk or saunter in
To show their strength and self-will.

All families crying but happy tears
To show that everything's gone but fears.
For everything that Man has done
We all still stand at the brunt of the gun.

Karalyn Gordon (13)
Culloden Academy, Inverness

My Ballad

Looking back they met in May
When everything was rosy
But now it is December
And things are no longer cosy.

They were with each other for a few months
And thought it would be forever
But sadly things went wrong
They each thought they would still be together.

The two of them grew apart
They went their separate ways
Then one day they met again
And it was just like always.

Then one day down on the beach
He knelt to his knee and pulled out a ring
She screamed yes
And started to dance and sing.

Rhianna Gibson (12)
Culloden Academy, Inverness

My Ballad

Once upon a time a boy called Lucky
Ate his toy dinosaur, it was yummy.
It was plastic and he nearly choked
If it wasn't for his mummy.

Lucky didn't realise
The dinosaur was magic
Lucky for him
This story isn't tragic.

Lucky became a hero
When a tragic fate unfurled
And Lucky with his powers
Saved the world.

Kalvin Mackenzie (13)
Culloden Academy, Inverness

Together For Evermore

The two lovers walked down the stream
They were only just together
They enjoyed each other's company when
They walked through the heather.

'I can't stand the two lovers'
Said the witch high up in the air!
She cast a spell to make them forget
And tossed back her straggly black hair!

When the lady and the man met again
And again they fell in love
The witch gave up and flew away
Oh so high above.

Jessica Wan (13)
Culloden Academy, Inverness

It All Ends Up In Prison

As the murderer walked away
From the women he had just killed
He didn't care about the blood
That he had just spilled.

Oh, I must get away
Thought the desperate man
And as the police chased after him
He ran to his van.

As the man went home
He heard a noise, it was a ghost
He had thought it couldn't be but it was
The very thing that he had feared the most.

As the man left his house the next day
By the police he was caught
And taken to prison
For longer than he thought!

Jason Scobbie (13)
Culloden Academy, Inverness

The Love Crisis

There were two men who were close friends
Their names were Ben and Jack
They never said a single cross word
They watched each other's back.

Until one day they both saw a girl
She was as beautiful as can be
The girl was in a gorgeous dress
They thought, *oh please choose me.*

The girl saw Jack and they fell in love
They stole each other's hearts
They got on perfectly together
They couldn't bear to be apart.

Ben found Jack and shouted at him,
'Why would you do this to me?'
Ben was upset and cried
Then he walked towards the sea.

A week later
Jack and the girl got married
The setting was lovely
Where the wedding was carried.

Later that day
Jack got a call
That his best friend Ben
Had died, Jack fell in his hall.

Rhianna Bell (12)
Culloden Academy, Inverness

Tom Clitz

Tom was walking on a misty day
He walked slowly all alone
A big group of gangsters saw him
They thought, *let's rip him to the bone.*

Tom looked behind him and saw them coming
He ran really fast
He ran fast for so long
He ran for so long he saw a man with a cast.

He pulled his mind away from the cast
But he was already too late
As he came closer to the cliff
He fell to his deadly fate.

The gangsters came to the edge of the cliff
They saw him hit a rock and splinter into bits
They saw the blood drip into the sea
The sea turned red with the blood of Tom Clitz.

'Sorry Ma'am but your son is dead
He fell and splintered into bits
I'm sorry about your son,'
Said the police officer to Mother Clitz.

Calum Murray (12)
Culloden Academy, Inverness

Days Of The Past

An old man sitting in his chair
His face weary with greying hair
Wondering why he was the one spared
When he didn't have anyone who cared.

Thinking of the days of the past
Many friends killed after another bomb blast
Lost limbs and lives became a daily sight
The guns ringing well into the dark night.

Never time for any well earned rest
Not even if you got a bullet through your chest
The sound of happiness seemed so far away
And every day to stay alive, you had to pray.

Every day less people would appear
This resulted in more bitter tears
Used to the pain, he became a recluse
He'd lost everybody there was to lose.

So here this old man bruised and scarred
Remembering when he was a guard
So loyal, he fought in the Great War
He'll remember those days for evermore.

Christy Macaskill (13)
Culloden Academy, Inverness

Forgotten

W hy are those who fight forgotten
A re they at war after the war?
R emembered people are the dead
T hough we do not complain because
I njured we may have been but in
M inds we came home, not stuck there
E ternally like those people

W e fought and were forgotten why
A nd now no one cares about us
R ight after we leave the army
T ime forgets the good, the bad, the
I njured, the brave, the sad. There are
M any still to come home dead
E nlighten them, it's not fun!

F orward that's the way they say
O r was it for the old me, OK?
R ight before the war, the deaths, those
G etting home didn't know what to do
O r who to trust back home but
T ough love that won't help me get home
T hey say you will be there with me
E ternally my mind says this
N o thanks, is my reply - I'm home.

Siobhan Pearson (13)
Culloden Academy, Inverness

Going Home

Going out to war
Not sure if you will come home
Waving your goodbyes.

Driving out to war
With all the friends you have made
Wishing them good luck.

Out in the fresh air
Stepping onto the battlefield
Stood in the trenches.

Thud of armies
The vibration in the Earth
Beneath our own feet.

The need to go home
Hoping to get through this one
And praying for friends.

Bombs flying everywhere
Obeying all orders
Seeing friends go down.

Searching for all your friends
Hoping they are here somewhere
Some aren't so lucky.

Travelling home, back home
The guilt of losing your friends
Traumatised by it.

Left with the war scars
On the inside and the out
Oh how it does hurt!

Anya Fraser (13)
Culloden Academy, Inverness

Haunting Memories

Remembrance Day is here
A painful and horrific day for lots
Parents grieving
Children crying
Friends remembering
The many lives that were lost.

But as well as deaths
There are those brave men
Who were once part of the army
Many injured, inside and out
Flashbacks, depression
Drugs, pain
All because of a job.

He thinks of his son
The guilt overwhelming
His life taken so early
The pain would never leave him
Seen a lot, been through a lot
Memories haunting.

Megan Hossack (13)
Culloden Academy, Inverness

My Ballad

'Beatrice I love you so much
I can't bear to be apart
You mean the world to me
You have my heart.

I will never last in this hospital
I am going to die
Beatrice please save me.'
Beatrice started to cry.

Then she met another man
Whose name was Jim.
If she had to pick between them
She would be sure to pick him.

Charles got out of the hospital
And opened the door
He was so happy that he was free
But then his jaw hit the floor.

'You have found another man.'
He grabbed a knife out of his pocket
'You will pay for my pain
I will take your life.'

Becca Grindell (14)
Culloden Academy, Inverness

Fredward And The Dragon

There was a humble bard named Fredward
A humble bard was he
He lived in a humble village
With his tiny family.

Young Fredward owned a tractor
He'd drive it every day
At this he was very skilful
He made a racetrack out of hay.

There lived a dragon
Up high, high hill
Which only Fredward
Knew how to kill.

He drove the tractor
Up the high, high hill
Where there stood the dragon
That Fredward would kill.

He drove the tractor into the dragon
And with a mighty bash
The dragon tumbled down the hill
And Fredward survived the crash.

Lewis Reid (14)
Culloden Academy, Inverness

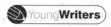

Fredward And The Crow

There was a lord named Fredward
A noble lord was he
But at time of writing
He had no family

But yonder high hills
A forest there stood
A hallowed place, an evil place
It was a haunted wood

As Fredward approached
The wood sprang to life
With howls of evil creatures
And Fredward drew his knife

There sprung a crow named Trudy
She would show him the way
And lead Fredward to safe passage
So long as he not stray

As the forest darkened
And the lane's end was drawing nigh
Fredward was startled
By an awful cry

A demon with eyes as black as night
And sharp claws like a crab
It ran to him with all its might
Fredward drew his knife and *stab!*

The demon lay wounded
But Fredward didn't yet know
That his attacker was in fact
Trudy the crow!

Trudy had betrayed him
Damn that blasted crow
How could he've been so naïve
If he had known.

Jack Reid (14)
Culloden Academy, Inverness

The Young Man And The Beautiful Woman

There was a man terribly in love
But he didn't know where to start
The most beautiful woman in town
Had completely captured his heart.

The woman was walking along the road
You could tell that she was fuming
This wasn't a good sight
After that a terrible fate was looming.

They met at an old corner shop
Where the woman practised her magic
When he saw her doing this
He exclaimed this is a tragic.

The young man didn't talk
And his reaction was very sad
The young woman tried to make him talk
But suddenly he went a bit mad.

The woman was so worried if the man would tell
But the man said he wouldn't tell
She said, 'Oh thank you, oh thank you
Do you want to see one of my spells?'

The young man said, 'Let's just be friends and not pretend.'
And now it is a happy end.

Samantha Reynolds [13]
Culloden Academy, Inverness

Death

There was a lady in the North
And found a man near the hillside
He looked so pale and fell so ill
Until she carried him home at midnight.

She sat him near the fireplace
And made him take medication
Then she made Jim clothes to wear
And then he had a conversation.

After all they were just friends
Who had just met at the mound,
He drove away in the dark, dark night
He felt dire and upset because of the sweet lady he found.

Oh why did I just drive away?
I should have stayed with her
I caused her trouble from the start
But now I have to forget about her.

He finally drove the hill
And decided to end his life
He took one jump and closed his eyes
And that was the end of his life.

The lady saw him on the news
Confused and too tired to believe
She said to herself one dull night,
'Why does it always happen to me?'

Yvonne Cornish (13)
Culloden Academy, Inverness

Death Ballad

Husband and his wife in their home
The husband is at the table being happy
'Oh how I like our new home'
While his wife was being soppy.

The husband steps up to his wife
'You need to grow . . . '
The wife didn't care
And she went to sew.

Next thing you see the door open
The husband comes with a knife
Wife gets worried and says
'Please don't, what about my life!'

The husband stops and looks at her
But he keeps to his plot
Then the neighbours called
As they heard a shot.

'You killed me with a gun
Now I must die!'
She breathed her last breath
With a huge sigh.

Nicola Alexander (14)
Culloden Academy, Inverness

Challenging The King

'I hate him, the king,
Him who killed my wife.
Now I'm going to kill him,
I'm going to do it with a knife.

I will kill him, I will kill him
Right in the middle of the fight.
I will not lose
Because I feel that is right.'

'You're a vicious young man,
I'm your king after all.
When we have our fight
To the ground you will fall.'

The fight has started, the end is near,
The king struck him with a vicious blow
Until he lost his sword
And knelt down low.

The man begs for forgiveness,
The king says with a harsh reply, 'No!'
The man is terrified
When the king shouts, 'Time to die!'

Jamie Cormie (13)
Culloden Academy, Inverness

My Ballad

There was a young knight
Whose name was Jack
He lived in a village with a nearby dragon
The village was scared of another attack.

The village had gathered around the centre
'I will go to the cave,' shouted the knight
As he raised his sword and shield
'And the village I will save!'

He saddled his horse, put on his armour
And started his travels to the cave
On his mind there were many things
But the village he must save.

After entering the cave
He found, asleep, the beast
And under it there was treasure
Enough to have many a feast.

As Jack crept slowly he stepped on a bone
The beast awoke, it raised its head
And the battle began
There was dodging and within minutes it was dead.

The hero returned with a welcoming cheer
The mayor walked up to him with a bag of gold
That had come from the cave.
The young knight became a hero and his title he would hold.

Harrison Wright (13)
Culloden Academy, Inverness

Christmas Dance

On one side of town
On a darkened street
There sat a young lady
With not a thing to eat.

On the richer side of town
He had the most wonderful house
The one thing he longed for
Was to find a lovely spouse.

It was Christmas Eve
All the people from the town
Came to the party, all the ladies
Dressed in the most beautiful gown.

The homeless lady showed up at the scene
In her rags she was such a sight
All the people stood and stared
Even some got a bit of a fright.

The rich man entered the party
He looked very smart
All the ladies turned to look
And he stole all but one's heart.

It was nearing the end of the night
And time for the final dance
The lady and man were now a pair
And they were already in a trance.

The man plucked up some courage
And asked the lady to get married
She said yes and the man picked her up
And out of the dance she was carried.

In the end they lived so happily
In the great house
The lady never slept
Next to another mouse.

Hannah Finlayson (13)
Culloden Academy, Inverness

The Prince And The Servant

On a very high mountain beside the blue sea
In a tall castle with brick walls that were grey
Lived a king and his royal family
They were out on the lawn playing croquet.

The king decided it was time to pass the throne to his son
'Now my dear son, which princess would you like as a wife?
I am holding a ball and every girl is coming,
There you will choose your princess for life.'

That night the prince danced with many beautiful girls
But near the end he spotted the one that was right
They danced together, staring deeply into each other's eyes
He thought about her for the rest of the night.

'Father, Father,' the prince said the next day.
'I know now, I have decided.'
'Go and bring her here,' the king demanded.
The prince ran out the door and he collided

To his amazement standing beside him was
The beautiful girl from last night
He took her by the hand and entered the room again
'Father, this is the girl that is right.'

'You can't marry her, she's a servant!'
'I know she is right and I want to marry her tonight!'
'You need to marry a princess or you will lose your throne!'
'Then I will lose my throne,' he said in delight.

'I will do anything just to be with my true love.'
The king took out a bag full of gold and gave them the whole thing
The prince's hand the queen took hold of and gave him a precious big ring.

The prince and his love walked out of the castle
And rode their horse into the sunlight
Leaving their parents with tears in their eyes
And they disappeared out of sight.

Karolina Huryn (13)
Culloden Academy, Inverness

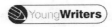

My Ballad

'Saddle your horse Jack,' said the queen
'And go to the market to see
I want you to fetch a golden necklace
The smith made for me.'

Jack sent off as the queen said
To fetch her necklace made of gold
Jack realised he had to pay for it
So he sneaked away with a firm hold.

Jack started to run away
And decided the necklace to keep
For himself, he meets a gap
In the Earth so takes a giant leap.

Poor Jack didn't make the leap
And had a terrible death
'He deserved it after stealing my necklace!'
The queen muttered under her breath.

Amy Rodgers (13)
Culloden Academy, Inverness

My Ballad

There were two brothers called John and Sam
But they never seemed to get on
Then something happened and it all went wrong.

Their father was a peaceful old man
Who lived at the top of a hill
But when he died
He forgot to leave a will.

'It's all mine!' said John.
With a bellowing shout.
'It's all mine!' said Sam
And gave John a clout.

They both had a fight
All the way through the night
And it was such a terrible sight
But they both died by first light.

So by first light
There was a terrible smell
There was no Sam and John
They both lay where they fell.

Bruce Flockhart (13)
Culloden Academy, Inverness

The Arrow Of Victory

I am dying my dear sons
I am going to leave you this arrow
When I fought in the Amazon
My escapes were very narrow.

Sons I say goodbye
Take this arrow in memory of me
Look after it well
Since it was my key to victory.

There their dad sat
Laying there like a bag of bones
Feeling such pain
It's near time to say goodbye in low tones.

Now their dad has gone
They fought a battle against each other
But both suffered a painful death
What bad brothers.

Sean Justin MacLeod (14)
Culloden Academy, Inverness

The Mystery

A hero was walking through the forest wild
When he saw a damsel under attack
Three soldiers threatened the maiden fair
He drew his blade and never looked back.

He whisked her away to a castle on high
Dazzled by her beauty he enquired of her name
'To learn of that you must vanquish a beast.'
'I fear no evil! This beast I will tame.'

'Ride far from here into the north
You will find a large cave where the beast does dwell
Slay this foul creature, for once and for all
Then my name to thee I will tell.'

Our hero set out the very same day
To learn of her name and this beast to be fought.
Upon reaching the cave he drew out his sword
And plunged deep inside with no second thought.

The monster fought hard, our hero did struggle
But with one last lunge he ripped out his heart
Exhausted and beat he rode back to the castle
To enquire of her name, now that he'd done his part.

The maiden did yell with surprise and delight
To learn of my name you have earned the right
And so with long flowing curtsies she started to say
'I am Princess Gloria, my dashing young knight.'

Hugo Iain Crush (13)
Culloden Academy, Inverness

Little Lucy

We were at the mall
We walked into a toyshop
Little Lucy saw a beautiful china doll
'Please Mummy,' Lucy pleaded.

As I took out my purse
Little Lucy clutched the doll tight
As I handed over a crisp note little did I know I was buying a curse
Little Lucy skipped out, eager to get home.

When Lucy and I got home, she was so pleased with her new doll
'Thank you so much Mum, I'm going upstairs,' said Lucy
Little Lucy sprinted up the stairs
As she shut the door her doll came to life!

'Wow,' whispered Lucy, 'it's magic?'
The china doll's eyes flickered and glowed
With the brightest shade of green
Little Lucy had no idea, this was to be tragic
Lucy flicked the light switch to see the green eyes more clearly.

An eerie green glow lighting the room, silence cut by humming
The doll was humming and suddenly the silence was stopped
And the doll spoke, 'I'm coming!'
'Aah, how cute,' Lucy said.
'5, 4, 3, 2, 1 . . .' All I heard was a scream!

I ran upstairs . . . took one look and started to cry
My little girl had been mashed by a china doll!
Why the doll had picked on my Lucy I will never know
Now I sit in jail accused of my daughter's death. I want justice . . .

Jenni Anderson (13)
Culloden Academy, Inverness

The Robbery That Went Wrong

King James was sitting down
In his dressing gown
When he saw people at his door
Wanting to steal his crown.

James called for his brother John
Telling him he was being robbed
John made his way to the castle
And saw James about to sob.

John killed one of the robbers
There was now only one robber left
John stabbed the other robber
And said, 'That's what you get for attempting theft.'

John helped James collect his belongings
James gave his crown to his brother
And said, 'Thank you for saving me
You are now the favoured son of our mother.'

Andrew Young (13)
Culloden Academy, Inverness

Grief

'My dear I tell you I must go away,'
The soldier said with remorse
'Must you go away?' begged she
But he'd ridden away on his horse.

As she watched him disappear
Onto her knees she fell
Till home she rode with a broken heart
And cried till twilight fell.

'So sad, so sad, so sad am I,'
The girl cried in sorrow.
'My dear why have you left me here
My insides have gone hollow.'

Years went by and the girl waited
But the soldier never returned
And each day she went to the place they parted
While the grief in her heart burned.

And so the girl who waited so long
Eventually surrendered to madness
She lay down where the couple parted
And there she died of sadness.

Vickie Baijal (13)
Culloden Academy, Inverness

A Story Where People Die And A Lot Of Pie

The surgeon told her, 'I'm so sorry'
She thought he deserved to be hit by a lorry.

She couldn't accept that her husband was dead
So she hit the surgeon over the head.

She baked him in a pie
When the police came she told a lie.

She said, 'Come in and don't be shy
Would you like to taste some pie?'

After dinner the police all felt sick
None of them realised she had played a trick.

She said to her children, 'I'm going for a walk in the rain.'
But really she was going to be with her husband again.

None of the children in this story did die
They all have a business selling pie.

Anna Wood (13)
Culloden Academy, Inverness

Three Is A Crowd

Darwin was charming
Tall, handsome and slim
And the girls would do anything
To be with him!

Darwin was out
When he met two sisters
They both begged him, 'Please -
Will you be my mister?'

Darwin grinned
A cheeky little smile
He looked down at their faces
And thought for a while.

They were both so pretty
How could he choose?
And suddenly it occurred to him
I've got nothing to lose!

He married them both
But make no mistake
For double the nagging
Was to be his fate!

Jenni Wood (13)
Culloden Academy, Inverness

My Ballad

A house is on fire
And it was caused by a wizard
No one knew where he came from
But he always arrived during a blizzard.

An angry scream came from inside
Just when the firemen arrived
Everyone was safe
As they all survived.

The boy was the wizard
And was accused for the fire
No one knew who he was
But they knew he was a liar.

The wizard ran away
Using his magic power
He disappeared into thin air
All was left was a bunch of flowers.

Mark Hammond (13)
Culloden Academy, Inverness

The Boy Who Told Lies

Tom was getting in trouble
For not sitting still.
The teacher was about to give him the belt
Until he blamed it on Bill.

Tom peeked through the window
To see Bill being whacked.
Tears streamed down Bill's face
So Tom ran back.

Tom was feeling really guilty,
He couldn't sleep at night.
He rolled and rolled
Until he saw the light.

The light was a ghost
Tom stood there with fear.
He ran and ran
Until the ghost wasn't near.

Tom was feeling really guilty,
Tears streamed down his face.
He packed his bags
And left the town in disgrace.

Bill went out and laughed at Tom,
I told him to stay.
Tom had been forgiven
But he still ran away.

Calum Hay (14)
Culloden Academy, Inverness

My Ballad

Years and years ago
Far in the land of Po
Lived an elf called Mo
Who fell in love with a pixie called Jo.

Pixies and elves don't mix
That's a well-known fact.
All the elves were happy
Until the secret cracked.

Everyone was angry
The goblins were going crazy.
The little elf was to be tied up
For falling in love with this lady.

The elf managed to escape
He found pixie and they both did go
Far far away
From the land of Po.

Sophie Gordon (13)
Culloden Academy, Inverness

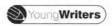

Mary And The Wolf

Mary was walking in the woods one day
Going back home from far, far away.
Mary had no idea what was about to happen
When her family was away home and napping.

Mary heard some noises and got rather scared
And thought that could maybe be a great big bear.
She walked faster and faster till she couldn't breathe
And came to a stop and started to wheeze.

Out of the middle of nowhere a wolf jumped out
And looked at Mary as if she was a trout.
The wolf attacked her and she started to scream
And started to wonder if it was just a dream.

Out of nowhere a man came to help
And gave the wolf a great big scalp.
The wolf ran away in fear
And then Mary said, 'Thank you, let's go get some beer!'

Charlotte Mackay (13)
Culloden Academy, Inverness

Some Families

Some families are good, some families are great,
Some families live in a state.
Marriage, settlement, divorce all the same,
Either way they're such a shame.
Some kids cry, some say bye,
Some kids just live a lie.
Some do things bad just because they're sad
But at the end of the day they've a right to be mad.
Some turn to drugs, some turn to hate
And some just don't turn out that great.
In spite of it all a family's love is great.
Some families are happy, some families are content
But some are only to a certain extent.

Chris Mercer (13)
Downshire Secondary School, Carrickfergus

George Best

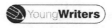

His name was George Best
He was better than the rest
He was born in east Belfast
And he was really fast.

He trained with a tennis ball
Then Manchester United gave him it all
He didn't cost that much
But my goodness there was certainly a lot of fuss!

He kicked the ball out of the keeper's hand
And in the back of the net it lands
Unfortunately he drank a lot of alcohol
Consequently from public grace he did fall.

When he was fifty-eight he sadly passed away
And everything changed in just one day.
His name was George Best
And he was better than the rest.

Daniel Walker (14)
Downshire Secondary School, Carrickfergus

Rugby In My Perspective

I love rugby
I love that competitive feeling
When every match has its meaning.

I love that each teammate is like a brother
Not one more than the other.

I love that sense of pride
When we all walk onto the pitch side by side.

I love the victory at the end of the year
When we all explode with a joyous cheer.
When it's worth all the blood, sweat and tears.

John Turner (13)
Downshire Secondary School, Carrickfergus

Irish Dancers

Irish dancers have . . .
Treble shoes
Wigs
Pumps
Dresses and make-up.

Irish dancers can be . . .
Very competitive
Very good
Very bad
Winners and losers.

Irish dancers can . . .
Compete in
Competitions
Ulsters
British Opens
Europeans
World Championships.

Irish dancers
Can be professional
Can become professionals
Are professional.

We are Irish dancers
And that's our lives.

Bethany Williams (13)
Downshire Secondary School, Carrickfergus

The Sea

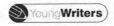

The sky was blue, the sea was calm
While sitting on the bay
The fisherman got in his boat
In the sunny month of May.

So off he went, he was on his way
To the middle of the sea
He cast his nets and began to sail
And all alone was he.

All of a sudden the sky turned black
The waves were vicious and tall
He wanted to turn back to the shore
But there was no time at all.

The enormous waves crashed into the boat
But there was nothing he could do
So he ran for shelter in the cabin
And prayed it wasn't true.

He lay inside defenceless
When the boat began to flood
The waves crashed into him one last time
With a great almighty thud.

He never returned back to the shore
As sad as this may be
As a warning to every fisherman
His ghost now haunts the sea.

Aaron Williams (13)
Downshire Secondary School, Carrickfergus

Football

The beautiful game
Is surrounded by fame
For players
To prayers.

The beautiful game
From the boot to the ball
They have got it all
The beautiful game.

The beautiful game
A footy fan loves his club
As much as his children or wife
The beautiful game.

The beautiful game
That goal
That makes football my soul
The beautiful game.

Bradley Spence
Downshire Secondary School, Carrickfergus

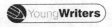

My Musical Instrument

Silver keys that shine in the light
Its voice is sweet and bright
Long and thin, standing with pride
I play it with joy
I hold it tight.

So gentle and fragile
When I take it out of its case
I link it all together
Its voice appears again
Sweet music in the air
So everyone can hear.

Lots of people watching
The tension builds up inside me
I think of all the wonderful memories
I try to play with confidence.

Jazz, blues, classical
They sound magical
The clarinet is so versatile
An instrument with class and style.

Christina Jefferson (14)
Downshire Secondary School, Carrickfergus

The Mad Old Woman

No one wanders too far down
The mug old street at number 13
No one dares to even look
At the foggy mist of death.

No one returns from the ones who dare
To wander into foggy mist
For those who dare to wander too far
The screams from the dead is all you can hear.

Every night when the clock strikes 12
Every dog howls and every cat screeches
As the mad old woman from number 13
Comes out to play.

Strange markings on streets
Street lights go out
Sweet becomes sour
Everything becomes so cold.

When the clock strikes one
Every dead soul bows down and
Prays to the mad old woman
As it returns to bay.

The mystery of the mad old woman
Still lies deep in everyone's mind
Since the death of Mary Jane
The mad old woman comes out to play!

Alison Loney (12)
Downshire Secondary School, Carrickfergus

Can You Imagine?

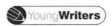

Can you imagine having no family?
No family to hug
No family to comfort you
And no family to talk to?
Imagine!

Can you imagine having no friends,
No friends to share secrets with,
No friends to laugh with
And no friends to love you like a brother or sister?
Imagine!

Can you imagine having no comforting pet,
No pet to greet you when you come home,
No pet to show you it loves you
And no pet to sit on your knee and keep you warm?
Imagine!

Can you imagine having no memories,
No memories to share,
No memories to smile or laugh at
And no memories like a blank page?
Imagine!

Can you imagine having no skills,
No skills to perform,
No skills to teach
And no skills to express who you are?
Imagine!

Can you imagine having no life,
No life to make choices in,
No life to smell or touch
And no life to experience anything?
Can you imagine?

Katie McCluskey (13)
Downshire Secondary School, Carrickfergus

Endangered Beauty

I look into those dark brown eyes
And see a gentle soul with claws and teeth.
Stop giving them grief - those poor beautiful animals.

The Arctic ice is melting away
And all the land animals have nowhere to stay
Those poor Arctic animals.

The tiger is another one, it used to run free
So much glee but now no more
The hunters came and shot that poor jungle animal.

There are many more animals.
I could go on forever but sorry I am not that clever.
But what is happening sends a shiver down my spine
For all those poor animals.

Aimee Swartz (12)
Dumbarton Academy, Dumbarton

Horses

An escape from every day stresses
An oasis of calm
Yet still so powerful.

A flurry of hooves create a heartbeat
A sound to behold
Yet still so docile.

A best friend when I need it most
A companion for life
Yet still so free.

So now I climb upon your back
And now we canter off
You're still so amazing.

Niamh Connolly (12)
Dumbarton Academy, Dumbarton

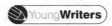

The Rainforest

In the morning the rainforest is peaceful
The only thing you can hear
Are the waterfalls and monkeys chattering far and near
The flashes of colour are so beautiful
But will it last?

In the afternoon there is a sudden bang
And out from behind the bushes the men sprang
With axes, saws and machines
They flatten down the land.

It is dusk and all around
Everything is dark
You cannot hear a sound
The animals have gone
They fled from the machines
Everything has vanished
Along with the trees.

Oona Gartshore (13)
Dumbarton Academy, Dumbarton

Football

The referee blows his whistle
On I run like a missile
In and out I weave through defence
I could have walked past, no offence!
In the box I cut inside
Thump the shot with power and pride.

I hear the crowd shouting, 'Goal!'
I'd burrowed through the defence like a mole
In and out with precision
And they say I need revision!

This is the best day of my life
I have had this in my sight
In my dreams and in my head
I am now a Manchester red.

Kyle McQueen (12)
Dumfries Academy, Dumfries

My Cat

My cat is important to me
He scratches at the door
He can even catch a bee
He also attacks the floor.

His name is Noz
He is quite fat
His favourite miaow is soz
Noz likes to chase the bat.

He is so cute
I should change his name to Juke
He loves to climb trees
He loves to bite my knees.

When I open the door to my house
My cat has probably caught a mouse
He would be on the couch
And he would be slouched.

Finley McLintock (12)
Dumfries Academy, Dumfries

Family

My family, you've got to love them!
There are funny ones and lazy ones,
Sad ones, bad ones and
The downright stupid ones!

My bashing bad bother of a brother
He sits around and moans all day
When I do nothing he just tells my mother
He walks in my room without my say.

My dad, he isn't funny
He just works all day long
My dad, he brings home the money
And luckily when we're out
He doesn't sing a song.

My mum, I couldn't live without her
She cooks, cleans, washes and minds
She has always said she wants a cat that goes purr
My mum, on herself she never spends.

Jemma Weir (12)
Dumfries Academy, Dumfries

Air

Air gives us life
Air gives us strength
Air gives us energy
And air gives us Earth.

Without it we would die
Without it we could fall
Without it we couldn't be alive
And without it we wouldn't stay in drive.

Air makes us live
Air keeps us going
Air can be good
But also it can be bad.

So the more air
The more living
The less air
The less living.

Rhys Harper (12)
Dumfries Academy, Dumfries

Life

Life is like a sentence
It has a start
A middle
And an ending.

It can be rewritten
It can be changed
It can be prolonged
And joined with another.

It has sad parts
Happy parts
Funny parts
And angry parts.

It can be long
It can be short
But what I know is
It is fun when it's lived.

Martin Reid (12)
Dumfries Academy, Dumfries

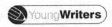

My Pet Mouse

My little mouse
Likes to live in his house
When he is gone I feel like a scone
I went outside today and I saw him running away.

He is called Hen
But he does hate Ben
Ben is a boy
That treats him like a toy.

He was on his wheel today
It was nice to see him running away
Every single day
Exercise all the way.

He broke out and escaped today
The vet said he would be okay
It's just another day
So my mouse is here to stay.

Ross Stuart Fergusson (12)
Dumfries Academy, Dumfries

Family

Family, family, family
They come in all shapes and sizes
Mine has eight legs and eleven paws
Which is four and three
And one with a dodgy knee.

Family, family, family
My family is super big
Eight aunts and six uncles
Which makes a lot of cousins
To help keep our parties swinging.

Family, family, family
My family goes on fantastic holidays
Clapping, packing, setting up and eating
We cry, smile, laugh and giggle
Sometimes even wriggle and wriggle.

Family, family, family
Time and time again
We have lots of fun together
Sadly as this poem ends
We think of those not here forever.

Neve Harkness McClurg (12)
Dumfries Academy, Dumfries

Tizzy

Tizzy you were one feisty kitten
I loved you
But you ripped my mittens!
You were also rough and tough
I loved you!

When you started getting fat
I realised that you were pregnant
I was happy because I was getting a kitten
And if I got new mittens you better not rip them
My sister called you a fat cat
I loved you!

You liked to play
You also like a sunny day
You hated it when it rained
But you liked it when it dribbled down the drains
I loved you!

Tizzy you clawed my lip, it hurt but I loved you
You knocked over a glass
And when I lifted you I ended up with fur on my top
But I loved you.

Your coat was so soft
That's why I loved you
After you stopped chasing the butterflies
You fell asleep on the grass
That's why I loved you.

Rachael Grier (12)
Dumfries Academy, Dumfries

Jet And Georgie

Jet you're a big fat lab
But you are so fab
Your coat is so smooth
You are very slow when you move
Jet you always get excited
For walks and your tea
When we get back you go straight to bed.
Georgie Porgie you're a wee stunner
When we let you off the lead you always do a runner
You moan and whimper when I am gone
When I am back you sing a song.

Georgie you're a delightful dumb dog
Who has no brain
We put your coat on in the rain
And you get lost in the fog
But I love you, Georgie.

Jet you love to play
You also love a nice sunny day
At night you snore
But through the day you lie at the door.

Jet you are ten
When you were a puppy you came into my den
Yet I love you with all my heart.

Jet and Georgie are the best
But mostly like to rest
You both make a good team
You also bark when you have a dream.
I love you Georgie and Jet
Although you stink when you get wet!

Tori Armstrong (12)
Dumfries Academy, Dumfries

My Mum

Let me tell you about my mum,
She is my very best chum.
She was born down under,
How she does everything I wonder.
Let me explain what she does,
On top of loves, loves and loves.
She cares, shops, does everything really,
And she does it all perfectly, daily.
Every time I'm in a muddle
She's there for me with a cuddle.
When there's a rough patch in front of me,
She smooths it out easily.
I can't describe how I feel,
How thankful I am for each meal.
I can't say the words in my brain
Although I try again and again.
Everything Mum does for me
I appreciate greatly.
I really hope that she knows
I love her from my head to toes.
She's an angel from above
And I send all my love.

Tiffany McGrogan (13)
Dunmurry High School, Dunmurry

Disasters Of The World

The world is such a beautiful place
But sometimes that's not the case.

Tornados whizzing
The trees burnt, sizzling
With the heat of the blazing sun.

Earthquakes shaking
Tsunamis awakening
Pollution upsetting our Earth.

Murder on the streets
People blaring very loud beats
Causing noise pollution today.

Meteors crashing
Robbers dashing
To get away from the crime.

Volcanoes exploding,
Guns reloading
Why can't we live in peace?

Emma Morton (14)
Dunmurry High School, Dunmurry

The Moon

The moon has a big white face.
The moon covers the human race.
It sparkles alongside the stars
And it lives near planet Mars.

I often gaze up at the moon
And see the surface shine and bloom.
When you look at it through a telescope it is so clear
It's hard to believe it's not quite near.

When the Earth's shadow covers the moon
The lunar eclipse is happening soon.
I love learning about the moon
I hope to travel to see it soon.

Sophie Torrans (14)
Dunmurry High School, Dunmurry

Football Fans

Football season is so exciting
Sometimes the fans end up fighting!
The love and the passion they have for the game
But the players now, all they want is fame.
Roaring and shouting, supporting their club
While drinking a beer in their local pub.
The fans look forward to the day
When one club will fly the winner's flag
The team that wins the Premiership
Gives their fans the right to brag!
This is the football season; football has gone to their heads
And their football scarves and beanies they even wear to bed!
Before the match they would all make a bet
Hoping that their team will put the ball in the net!

Jamie English (14)
Dunmurry High School, Dunmurry

One That Got Away

Last weekend I went fishing
With my dad off to the lake
We packed our gear and off we went
To catch fish, just for our plate.

I wanted to catch a big one
Not let it get away
So I waited and I waited
For that fish all day

I felt a pull, it was my line
My monster fish had bit
This fish was big, I could tell
It surely was a hit

I felt my rod pull left and right
That fish it fought like mad
I needed help, I can't hold on
Just where's my lazy dad?

At last, at last, I saw my fish
Its head came to the top
It jumped and turned and pulled again
Then my line began to flop.

I've lost my fish, my monster fish
Can't believe it's got away
Nothing to show yet again
Fishing fever is all I caught that day.

Ryan Mack (14)
Dunmurry High School, Dunmurry

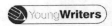

What Is Friendship To Me?

Friendship to shine like the sun
Friendship to make you number one
Friendship to hold on tight
Friendship to turn on the light
Friendship is the key
Friendship is close to me
Friendship is love to say
Friendship is love to shout today
Friendship lasts forever and is never undone
Friendship has only begun
Friendship stays as sweet as can be
Friendship is something to search for and to see
Friendship goes on until I fade away
Friendship is words to say
Friendship to stay by your side till the end
Friendship is my best friend
Friendship to find and call
Friendship is the best of all
Friendship is something I want close to me, not apart
I want to be friends and keep you somewhere special in my heart.

Chantella Mitchell (14)
Dunmurry High School, Dunmurry

Valentine's Day

The colour of love is the colour red,
Love is the food that the heart is fed.
When you see the one you love your heart beats fast
And all you do is pray that this feeling will last.

The symbol of Valentine's Day is the rose,
You give it to the person who stands out and glows.
When you see them you crack a smile,
If you fight for them it's worthwhile.

When you see them you bubble up inside
But all that love you try to hide.
You just hope they feel the same way
And if you ask them, they say you may.

So go on and ask them out
Don't have a single doubt.
Make sure you do it now
Are you ready to make that vow?

Dylan Sinclair (14)
Dunmurry High School, Dunmurry

Eternal Love

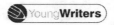

Eternal love one more to say
A candle lit for you to pray.
Eternal love to follow you and find
Something is not far behind.
Eternal love watching from coast to coast
I'll grab the love because it is what I need most.
Eternal love when I call
No matter what it will catch me when I fall.
Eternal love to flow and see
It's the love I want close to me.
Eternal love is time for celebration
As you open your heart to salvation.
Eternal love to close your eyes and pray
Something is changing every day.
Eternal love will never stop because this is just the start
This love is special in my heart.
Eternal love takes you a long way to go
Love is water to slide and flow.
Eternal love is your guard to stand
For I take the love and hold your hand.
Eternal love will keep hold of you from strength to weak
Because eternal love is the thing to seek.
Eternal love open your heart to see what's inside
I want to know what to do, not hide.
Eternal love means love will give you eternal love day by day
Love gives you direction in every way.
Eternal love is a lovely sensation
And I'll tell the nation.
Eternal love I'll walk to the place in the high rays
And I will jump and sing the praise.
Eternal love will stay there in my heart so high
I'll keep that love in my pocket when I die.

Melissa Patty (14)
Dunmurry High School, Dunmurry

The Irish Famine

To remember when time was good
When all was well and there was food
And now we might as well be dead
Because of famine we won't be fed.

Now to the soup kitchen, it's all I've got
The cold brownish soup in the pot
Children are crying, begging for more
As some too weak fall to the floor.

I'm on my own, my family are dead
The children I love, the husband I wed
And now I wish I was on my way
To Heaven, to paradise at the end of the day.

Now to the workhouse I must go
The low amount of food I tow
Although the workhouse is not a treat
Well at least there's a bed and something to eat.

Daisy Joy Pollock (12)
Glenlola Collegiate School, Bangor

She's Gone

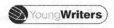

I stand at the brim of the cliff ready to jump
Hoping that she'll be there to catch me when I fall
I jump, the cold air wraps around me,
Suffocating me as I fly.

I hit the ground with a thud!
She is not there at all.
My bones are slowly seizing,
My eyes are slowly closing,
My heart is slowly stopping.

I look towards the east, she is not there
But over to the west and there she is
Catching someone else
And running with her hand-in-hand
She does not see me lying there
And just tramples over me instead.
She has found someone to replace me,
To be her new best friend.

She does not know I'm here
But I'll always be here for her
Even though she has hurt me and broken me
(And tried to destroy me)
I'll be here for her.

I close my eyes and lie here in the dusty silence
Until I see her running back
But I know she never will because
She's gone.

Steffi McCormick (13)
Glenlola Collegiate School, Bangor

Nails

They are sticking there for all to see
They are a bit of a reflection on
Naughty
Me.

All those hours painting
On and lots of thing to think upon.

And the counter lady always tutts
As I pile my Barry M onto the checkout.

Every colour you can imagine,
I pick and try
I have so many I want to cry.

They don't even fit in the bag anymore
So I have to lay them on the floor,
Wall to wall I watch them grow as I open them onto
My nails they flow, flow, flow.

But as I sit here
Writing this
I realise what I've missed.
Those things in life that make you smile
Mostly those things only stay a while.
And life itself all on its own;
My family, summertime,
A good book to read or maybe just
Simple me.

My nails now are bare
And I'll throw the polish out, just to see
If they really are what's important to me.

Grace Russell (13)
Howell's School, Denbigh

What Matters To Me?

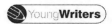

I
Don't
Know
What
Matters
To
Me.
There's too much choice to put a spotlight on anything,
But at the same time the spotlight's on everything.
Everyone.
I wouldn't be able to live without my friends and family,
Or shoes.
But that is what matters.
I think.
People say the most difficult things in life are decisions.
I agree.
Choosing what matters could be easy.
Imagine it's the end of the world,
Who would you save
Or what?
I don't know.
I guess it's one of those last minute decisions
Or is it just me?

Questions,

Questions,

Questions.
Only
One
Answer.

Emily Adey (12)
Howell's School, Denbigh

What Matters To Me?

At times my
Worst enemy
At times my
Best friend
No.
She's my sister.
Like a diary she'll keep my secrets,
Like a blanket she'll keep me warm.
Her smile could
Lift
A snowfall
Her tears could
Sink
A ship.
Under this first class
Disguise
She is really quite plain.
A handful of
Dreams
And feeling.
But most of all the
Love
She
Receives.

Emily Vawdrey (13)
Howell's School, Denbigh

I Take My Last Look Around

I take my last look around
At the sun and at my home
I listen to the birds sing to each other
I feel the bitterness in the air.

Cries are let loose, neighbours think this is their last breath,
Their expression is like a diary,
A gradual fast flow of water plumbs through the streets.
Reality has happened.

The rising of the sea floods over the banks,
Cars and children's toys float away,
We are not safe,
The Earth has been destroyed by us selfish people.

Scared and anxious as I watch the steel machines run through the sky,
Confused people listen for an answer.
They tell us we are saved.
People climb on board, rushing and shouting, trying
To get away from the horror behind.

A sigh of relief comes to me.
Dead bodies are beneath us.
They could have been me.
I could have been dead, a shiver is sent down my spine.

Chloe Young (16)
Howell's School, Denbigh

The People Stood Still

The people stood still
Like the towers before them.
It was cold but got colder.

My place in the world war
Ought to be forgotten. Forever.
Nothing would be left but our memories.

The rockets left.
I was on one.
Millions left for their fight.

I didn't know where we were going.
I still don't.
No one knows what will happen next.

I smile. I'm safe.
But others are not.
The Earth will one day stand still.

The swings built for children's happiness,
Gone. Our own home, our own space,
Gone. What will I miss?

Everything. The blue cloudless sky.
A calm grey sky. The colour of trees.

Hannah Moore (16)
Howell's School, Denbigh

Flapping, Heart-Shaped

Flapping, heart-shaped wings, the butterfly emerges
From the crumbling castle window,
Settles herself and dries her wings
In the heat and light of our star,
She blends, safe, against the tree.
Sweet apples hang from her branches.
Leaves spread like friendly, open arms,
Stable and grounded as her roots,
Delve into the rich Earth,
Her roots holding her,
For it is our roots that ground us all.
You have let your generations lose grip
Of the Earth,
Letting your roots die little by little.
I expect your science will keep your tree alive.
But your science killed it too.
And now your roots can't hold on
To your Mother Earth,
Because you all went too far.
So desert us now, we're dying.
Leave us all to die.

Ruth Ng (16)
Howell's School, Denbigh

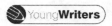

You Do Not Know This

You do not know this.
The story of what was before
Beasts relied on nature and nature relied on beasts.
The water of the world like a transparent window.
Fresh smells of blood and sweat
Food was enough.

Straw, sticks, wood . . . brick
We found our source for shelter's strength.
Crisp paper danced in our hands
To the sound of the harmonious tunes
Everlasting colours draped from our bodies.

I did not know this,
That what we had before would soon be no more.
The fish's home covered by funeral's silk.
The nightingale would no longer sink.
The farmer's work would bring him dust.

Thunder and lightning burst from the grounds
Ahmed deafened to the lion's roar.
Flowers and trees bowed in unison.
The Pope had no say
Bricks, wood, sticks . . . straw.

Einstein and Darwin could not have comprehended.
Books and machine were of no value
Mr Beacon and his family were evacuated
Religion claimed judgement had come.

Stories upon stories still unfold
The truth was what we failed to acknowledge: 'Thank you'
Mother Earth did not hear from us
At the time; we did not know this.

Joanna Appleby (16)
Howell's School, Denbigh

What Matters To You?

I have a question
But I don't know what to say
It's like how long is a piece of string or when will I die?
But those questions can be shortened to my liking.
But my question is what matters to you?
I don't know what matters to me,
So I have to ask, what matters to you?
Lots of people say family, pets or yummy sweets
Or some wise people say love or life.
Some people say silly things like rocks or an electronic game.
But what's the point of that?
I think . . . I know what mine is but I really don't
Could it be myself? But that's really selfish . . .
Is it?

Saffron Yates (13)
Howell's School, Denbigh

Dreamy Daze

The bus stop atmosphere shivers down my spine,
As I stand lazily queuing in the bus line.
While my journey goes on and on and on
My mind wonders about someone.

The bus gives me a sudden jolt
It slows right down and comes to a halt.
People push by with elbows and bags
Bodies squash in and the driver he nags.
A huge sigh enters my mouth
When the journey decides to carry on south.

My travels end in Broadaxe Lane
With no one on the bus acting sane.
Ear phones fall from behind my hair
As I step off the bus without a care.

The day goes on through thick and thin,
I must make sure I'm listening!

Siân Vincent (12)
John Beddoes School, Presteigne

My School Topics

Geography, Welsh,
RE and history,
These are the topics
That don't shed light on me.

Tech, science,
Music and maths,
These are the topics
That make me laugh.

PE, art,
English down the hall,
These are the topics
I love most of all.

These are the topics
I love and hate,
So I've just got to hope
For some I won't be late!

Kira Lloyd-Bithell (12)
John Beddoes School, Presteigne

Sports Day Nightmare

Sports day and they all look glum
But worse you're told you have to run
Your flying hair, your legs bare
The wind blowing, the drinks flowing
Catching breath, nearly at death
Inhalers puffing, kids bluffing
Ice creams all round, winners are crowned
Next year's round the corner, people thinking of the trauma
Of the next year's sports day
What a sarcastic, *hip, hip, hooray!*

Anna Morgan (12)
John Beddoes School, Presteigne

Travelling Through School

The first day at school is always so weird,
Meeting the headmaster with that awful grey beard.
The little young darlings are always loud,
You write your first word and your parents are proud.
Then the Nativity, the night when you are opposite to Devil,
My mate, John, waving to his mum Mrs Bevil.
Milk time is great,
The time when no one is late.
You sit in class just glaring with both eyes fixed on the clock
Waiting for playtime, then the teacher calls your name
And you jump up in shock.
On the playground where you can break free
Run, jump, skip, fly high like a bumblebee.
Before you know it, primary is behind you
Those myths about high school
Getting your head flushed down the loo.
It's a time for friends not to fight and fall out,
They are the main things in life without a doubt
So here's to the next few years in JB
We will never forget these years in school, hopefully!

Lily-May Pebbles Banbury-Pugh (12)
John Beddoes School, Presteigne

Fear

Yesterday, he came
Patting on my shoulder,
The darksome man
Herr Fear.

I turned round
Looking in his eyes:
Grey, deep, empty
Like me, a dust.

He took a step
And I realised that
He had followed me a long time,
My shadow,

A part of me,
Inside and outside,
Tapping on my back
Again, again.

He likes darkness
And lonely evenings
When no one is here
To blow him away,

Far, far away.
Hope he won't find me,
The spiteful fake
Monsieur Fear,

The private detective
Spying on my life,
And his impatient client
Fräulein Madness.

Martina Lejskova (16)
Lomond School, Helensburgh

Is Anyone Listening?

Waking to the tears left the night before,
My pillow a constant wetness on this eternal floor.
The thought of getting up to that poisonous place,
The reminiscing smack being brought across my face!

I lie awake throughout the night,
Praying to God to cease the morning light.
To delay it a little so I can be with my friend,
Because the moon does not judge me, no hurt does it intend.

The names I chant in my head each day,
The black and blue veins a symbol to stay.
What have I done to deserve this hurt?
My heart torn apart as well as my shirt.

My tie they tell me could make a better use,
I should wrap it around and use it as a noose.
My family they know nothing about what I go through,
Deep inside I want to shout to ask them what to do.

But the bullies say they'll kill me if their secret is let out,
I long for a chance to ask them what's this all about?
Is it that my skin is less superior than them?
Because of my religion which they feel they can condemn?

My day feels like a soundless film with silent screams locked away,
I need someone to take my hand and guide me on my way.
But now I've found my voice inside, is anyone listening to me
Or will we be oblivious to life, and live ignoring what we see?

Michaela Quinn (17)
Lurgan College, Lurgan

Not In The Brochure

Callously trailed out of lorries and cars,
Leaving gashes and wounds which fail to heal;
Then bartered and bought like pets at bazaars.
Battered, then thrown into a room of bars,
As pain penetrates and she hates to feel;
Whilst looking through greasy glass at the stars,
She is grabbed, drugged; then all becomes surreal.
Now, abused and alone, burnt by cigars,
And wearing bloodstained clothes, ripped to reveal;
Today's blackened bruises, slashes and scars,
And brutal beatings she cannot conceal.

Between tears she thinks of the life she fled,
With persecution and living terror;
Fantasies of hope which then lay ahead,
Now she is trapped inside this cellar.
Her tears rain in rivets upon the bed,
On which she lies frozen - pained with hunger;
Her brothers and sister sleep looking dead,
And for more heat she moves slightly closer.
The terrifying truth she had heard said
Is that she will remain in this chamber;
Until she is released and ransom paid,
She will serve those who trafficked and tricked her.

Darren Ferguson (16)
Lurgan College, Lurgan

Distorted Beauty

Let go of all the things they've made you believe
That to survive - silence is key
Yet it's the lock that keeps you suffering
A worthless reflection becomes your identity,
A false reality.
Take off the clothes that are counterfeit
Reveal who you are and the worth found in it.
Nobody can create the beauty of boldness
No image can break the spirit of faithfulness
Take off everything that you don't want to be
Like a captive being set free
Releasing faith to take the unseen hand
And pull you out of this sinking sand.

For what seems impossible, will be yours to hold.
What you once thought was dirt, will soon turn to gold.

Kathryn Stevenson (18)
Lurgan College, Lurgan

My Name

My name is Jonathan or Jonnie.
My name sounds simple.
My name is the colour blue like a summer's sky.
It feels like an American name when people say it.
If my name was a number it would be 10.
If my name was an animal it would be a bobcat.
My name Jonnie makes me feel happy.

Jonnie Woods (11)
Omagh High School, Omagh

I Am One Who Is

I am one
Who is gentle,
Who loves the sound of waves
Hitting the rocks at night
And the feeling of being happy.
Who dreams of looking after her family,
Who is good at making people smile,
Who fears about people she cares about being in danger,
Who cares about family and friends,
Who will someday be a hero.
I am Melodi and that makes me me!

Melodi Somerville (12)
Omagh High School, Omagh

I Am

I am one who is friendly, energetic and not shy.
Who loves the sound of Clubland and Ministry of Sound
With the feeling of happy and joyful.
Who dreams of becoming a hairdresser or a make-up artist.
Who is good at being a dependable friend.
Who fears spiders.
Who cares about my friends and family.
Who will someday be a street dancer.
I am Courtney and I am glad to be me.

Courtney Ross (12)
Omagh High School, Omagh

I Am

I am one who is happy and friendly
Who loves the sound of horseshoes on the ground
Who dreams of being in the netball team
Who is good at cooking and taking care of horses
Who fears falling off horses
Who cares about horses and my family
Who will someday be a horse rider
I am Laura-Ann and I like my name.

Laura-Ann Stewart (11)
Omagh High School, Omagh

Me!

I am one who is friendly, sporty and artistic.
Who loves the sound of JLS, One Direction and The Saturdays
And the feeling of playing hockey while the wind blows through my hair.
Who dreams of becoming an actress or teacher.
Who is good at sports.
Who fears spiders.
Who cares about my family and friends.
Who will someday have horses and dogs.
I am always myself and I'm proud of it.

Nicole Breen (12)
Omagh High School, Omagh

The Flower - Haiku

Flowers are so bright
The flowers petals are red
Ow, how they shine bright.

Jordan Amos (11)
Pontypridd High School, Pontypridd

Wales

Wales is so cool,
If you don't like it you're a fool.
Red, green and white
With these colours we will fight.

Welsh rugby is good
Try it, you really should.
There are lots of landmarks
From mountains to car parks.

The football is alright
We go out to clubs every night.
Our main animal is sheep,
That's all they do is bleat.

The border is a river
Separating us from a liver.
We have our own language,
Welsh is that language.

Owain Morris (12)
Pontypridd High School, Pontypridd

My Welsh Sonnet

We are Welsh, in our blood we are farmers
We have cows but we are meant to have sheep.
We are Welsh so we don't have llamas
We're not high-tech but we have daffodils.
We found our land and turned it to Wales,
Once the farm was done, the sheep came to us.
We were Celts so we sometimes use flails
The land was English now it is Welsh.
We have terrible weather and things go poof
We lose our flock to the thundering weather.
The evidence is there so we don't need proof.
We travel up hills and find them the next day.
I still think that Wales is the very best
I should know 'cause I live in the south-west.

Daniel Kai Shoemark (11)
Pontypridd High School, Pontypridd

Welsh Food Sonnet

Welsh food is my favourite in the world
It tastes really nice and kind of spicy
Though none of our food is really curled
Welsh food is still the best food in the world
We have got loads of different foods here
In our great and lovely country, Wales
It is really nice but it may occur
That our lamb is sometimes spiced with herbs
But I'm not a big fan of our meats
With the herbs and spices all together
Though nothing in this great world really beats
A Welsh cake on a nice night like tonight
Though not all of our food is really great
Our Welsh food will always be my mate.

Brandon Jeffs (11)
Pontypridd High School, Pontypridd

Rugby Team

Wales have an amazing rugby team
When they score we all jump and gleam.
The crowd is so big
We all do a jig.
The amazing Welsh rugby team.

Paige Llewellyn John (12)
Pontypridd High School, Pontypridd

Wales Sonnet

The sheep lay on the top of mountains
While the colourful flowers grow tall.
There the water throws out of the fountains
While the rain floods down on the mountain.
The most famous one of all - Snowdonia
Water flows down every day, down to the river.
Some of them are big but lonely
And some with lots of snow on top of them.
They have some mud slides which are slimy
People slide down the mountain when they walk
When people walk up the mountain it's climby
Everybody laughs when they get a bit muddy.
We all still love our mountains
We all still get wet by the fountains.

James Williams (11)
Pontypridd High School, Pontypridd

My Welsh Sonnet

I love the very good Welsh rugby team
It's always a big time when games are on
Stadium always packed with lots of fans
I want them to win, so I'm always very keen!
Shanklin was a very good famous player
He scored a lot of tries for the Welsh team
Even though he didn't have much hair
I like it when the final whistle goes
Sometimes Wales do lose very badly
We haven't got the team we used to have
Wales haven't done very good lately
They were better than what we have now
We love our rugby team when they play
Sometimes they perform very good on the day
We still think that our rugby team's the best
No matter how they do on the day.

Dylan Wert (12)
Pontypridd High School, Pontypridd

My Welsh Haikus

Sheep which graze the grass
Live on all of the mountains
Giving birth in spring.

The tall Welsh mountains
Which the river flows downwards
Always keeps its life.

Rhys Lacey (12)
Pontypridd High School, Pontypridd

Welsh Haikus

This is our land, Wales
With all the fluffy, white sheep
And all of the hills.

Wales is where I live
Between the mountains and hills
Down in the valleys.

I live in a town
Which is known as Pontypridd
Where it always rains.

This is a country
The capital is Cardiff
This is our land, Wales.

Kyle Aalten (12)
Pontypridd High School, Pontypridd

Dangerous Love For The Perilous Cliffs

The whistling peaks of Welsh mountains so refine
Stand tall as I gaze into the horizon.
My love for them is glowing red and divine
Their solid structure cannot contain it.
The wondrous mounds of lovable landscape
Reaches beyond my deep expectations
My desire cannot be rid of or escape
The possibility would be impossible
The winds could battle to disturb my love
The words I speak cannot fell the dangers
The icicles of winter may fall from above
Sometimes my compass changes direction
The temptation of fleeing away from it
Won't shake the compassion, my heart will tame it.

Simon Lee Humphries (12)
Pontypridd High School, Pontypridd

Swansea City Sonnet

I really love that stadium roar
When the super Swans come out to play
When they play their football we want more
We shout and shout till the game runs out.

As I walk up the steps to get my seat
As we see the players running out
Dribbling the ball at their feet
That is all that we like to see.

As we all arrived at the ground
To watch the City play
It was an amazing sound
Then the team started to play
That's what I love to see
And then I go home for my tea.

Jack Shaddick-Woodman (12)
Pontypridd High School, Pontypridd

Wales Limerick

There was a man who lived in Wales
He had stood on lots of nails.
The man started crying
That is not surprising
He was a total fail.

Morgan Jones (12)
Pontypridd High School, Pontypridd

Sonnet About Wales

We wear big black bonnets on our heads
And cotton checked dresses on our bodies
Because of the Welsh saint who now is dead
We celebrate our Saint David's Day each year.
Our great smelly green leeks on our Welsh shirts
And our bright yellow daffodils.
We all wait for this day for weeks and weeks
It's a time we come together, taking part
Some are putting on a show to entertain
There are some people singing and dancing
Though in the back row it can be a pain
Cos you can't see with the people in front
Everyone gathering, some small, some tall,
So much of us lot we fill the school hall!

Angel Lock (12)
Pontypridd High School, Pontypridd

Wales Sonnet

With people calling us the Land of Song
With all the singers coming from Wales
Singers have been from Wales for so long
But we'll let no one get between the Land of Song
They have been inspiring us all the time
Making their hometown very proud of them
We hear their songs and sing along to every line
Making us dance around the kitchen
But when we hear they have done something wrong
We think that they should not come back to Wales
After a while this is where they belong
Because they are Welsh through and through
From Duffy to Tom Jones our Welsh singers
They travel around but in Wales they linger.

Emily Davies (12)
Pontypridd High School, Pontypridd

Welsh Limericks

Beautiful gardens of Wales
Why haven't you heard the tales?
The daffodils are blooming
The big yellow sun is booming
But actually this fails.

Rain, rain it needs to go away
It's not time for you today.
Giant puddles
Which hold a lot of cuddles
It is not meant to rain today.

Olivia Edwards (11)
Pontypridd High School, Pontypridd

Welsh Sonnet

Baa go the beautiful Welsh sheep
Their fluffy white coats are as soft as wool
They look as wonderful as clouds when they leap
They're so peaceful when they sleep in the field
Welsh sheep are so beautiful when they're lambs
They grow up just like you and me
They drink their water by the beaver dams
The beavers don't mind, they are good at sharing
Poor sheep, the farmers kill them for food
You feel sorry for them in a way
When you eat their meat it puts you in a bad mood
You don't think about when you eat, only after
My love for the gorgeous white fluffy sheep
I will not stop loving them until they sleep.

Mary Clarke (12)
Pontypridd High School, Pontypridd

Wales

There is a small country, Wales,
It has some powerful gales.
There are lots of sheep
Up to the highest peak
That is the country called Wales.

Dafydd Harvey (12)
Pontypridd High School, Pontypridd

How I Am So Proud To Be Welsh

Here we are in the valleys of Wales
Bright green leeks shining in the sun
Unfortunately there are no big blue whales
How I am so proud to be Welsh
Our Welsh flag flying high
With the bright red fierce dragon
Flying high across the sky
How I am so proud to be Welsh
I love going to watch the Welsh game
Especially when Wales win
I absolutely love Shane Williams' name
How I am so proud to be Welsh
Me and my friends love having Welsh cakes
How I am so proud to be Welsh.

Samantha Davies (12)
Pontypridd High School, Pontypridd

A Welsh Poem

I love our Welsh dragon with his red scales
And his white pointy teeth that breathes fire
And he has a very long thumping tail
With his darted claws that are like razors.
I also love and like the food here.
Like the very nice home-made Welsh cakes
Watching your mother make it as you mix and stir
'Ymm,' I say as I'm eating one
Unfortunately here there's hardly any sun
It is always raining all the time
It really does tons and tons and tons
How I wish the weather could change
But however, I still love you Wales.

Kayla Samuel (11)
Pontypridd High School, Pontypridd

Wales

W ales is a land of rugby
A place of song
L and of valleys with fluffy sheep
E merging through the clouds comes a rainbow
S mall but special, Wales is clearly the best!

Rhiannon Moore (11)
Pontypridd High School, Pontypridd

A Little Place Called Wales

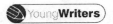

There is a little place called Wales
It has so many great tales
Its rugby is fun,
Its food is so yum
That little place, Wales, never fails.

Alix Jones (12)
Pontypridd High School, Pontypridd

Wales - Haiku

Wales is very fun
Lots to do even in snow
Wales is very cool.

Daniel Morgan (11)
Pontypridd High School, Pontypridd

My Welsh Poem

Rugby is our nation's sport
We play it for the love and joy
We put in a lot of thought, that's why we win a lot.
We sing our songs with pride
It fills our stadium with lots of joy.
Our fans make our players warm inside
And they make the stadium go wild.
Even though we lose sometimes
We stick together all the time,
We pull through the hard times.
If we lose we say, 'Oh well'
We will always love our rugby team
That's why we are proud to be Welsh.

Sam Burgess & Jack Archer (12)
Pontypridd High School, Pontypridd

Why We Love Wales

Wales is a place for rugby
We help the players by supporting
We win some games because we are lucky
That's why we love Wales.

The stadium makes us happy
When Wales win in rugby
We scream and shout, *'Hooray!'*
That makes us proud to be there.

Sometimes we lost a lot of games
It doesn't matter because we tried.
There is always another game to go,
It is disappointing but we still love Wales.

I am proud to be Welsh,
That's why I love Wales.

Morgyn Thompson (12)
Pontypridd High School, Pontypridd

Silly Sheep

Long fluffy tail of a sheep
Swaying back and forth
Like a dandelion weeps.

Cold as this day
The sheep walk away
With cold hands, legs and feet.

It's big and fluffy
And leaves loads of mess
Oh, it's smelly,
I don't want to clean it next!

Callum Griffiths (11)
Pontypridd High School, Pontypridd

Wales Rugby

Our Welsh rugby is just the best
When we sing our national anthem.
In the game they're as good as the rest
I feel so proud to be Welsh.

The stadium they play in stands out from all
The sun shining down bright
And across the field spins the rugby ball
The welsh flag high in the sky.

We might have lost a few games
But in the end it was a test.
But our strength always came
That's how we are the best.

Even though we are so poor
Wales I love you more and more.

Sarah Lethbridge (12)
Pontypridd High School, Pontypridd

Water - Haiku

Water in my bath
Can you hear it splashing loud?
Water shines in light.

Clara Bird (12)
Pontypridd High School, Pontypridd

My Welsh Sonnet

This is my sonnet about Welsh rugby
Love playing rugby for Ynys-ybwl
Love watching Wales play rugby on TV
I really, really, really love rugby

Everyone sings the Welsh anthem at games
Even the players on the pitch sing it
Most true fans even go to away games
Wales is the best on Earth to the Welsh.

Even though we lose a lot of games
Even though Twickenham is bigger than ours
The pitch in the stadium is small for games
The bad thing about Wales is it is small

But whatever happens I still love Wales
Even though we have absolutely no whales.

Ieuan Jones (12)
Pontypridd High School, Pontypridd

My Welsh Limerick

There is a place called Wales
We are as tough as nails.
We got a good team
As big as we seem
There is a place called Wales.

Dewi Jones (11)
Pontypridd High School, Pontypridd

My Welsh Poem

Welsh pride, Cardiff City, Wales high
The Cardiff City stadium roars
Screaming supporters praying to the sky
My love for the game begins here
Bellamy and Chopra bursting down the line
Screaming, shouting, Dave Jones on the side
Screaming Ramsey squealing that it's mine
Rhyming chanting songs fly around the sky
Even though we lose sometimes
And miss our easiest chances
Heartache in Wembley chimes
Premier League we still cry
I love Cardiff City, nothing else I pray
Pride, passion and others too, I love Wales and Cardiff too.

Lewis Wells (12)
Pontypridd High School, Pontypridd

Welsh

In the country that first developed the train
In rolling hills and jagged mountains
Where it never ceases to rain
The country never ceases to please.

The largest mountain in England and Wales
Some railway breakthrough that changed the world
And we live in this country through rain and gales
To enjoy the times of fun and calm.

We live amongst poverty
And suffer from a deep depression
We pretend to be all strong and mighty
And they did ignore the unfortunate

In the country that is famous for the coal mine
We battle it all, come rain or shine.

Jocelyn Kress Churchill (12)
Pontypridd High School, Pontypridd

The Love Of Welsh Rugby

Oh how I love the sport of Welsh rugby
Standing, sitting in the stadium
The Welsh love of rugby is inside me
Listening to the Welsh squad and fans sing.

When they play I throw on my jersey
Holding the badge when they're on the burst
Then they get fouled and score the penalty
Celebrating when they win the grand slam.

But even though they lose a lot
They take a battering from Ireland and France
They don't use all of the strength that they've got
This is really devastating for me

Even though they lose by a heap
No one will ever take the love of Welsh rugby from me.

Dylan Griffiths (11)
Pontypridd High School, Pontypridd

Christmas Wonderland

Christmas snowflakes falling from the dark breezy sky
A big man all snuggled up in his warm, cosy winter coat
Strutting down the dark lawn.
Deep soft snow blankets the mushy ground
A robin perched on a freezing wall
All lonely and cold, a warm-glazing fire
Lit right in front of the sparkling green tree.

Sound of longing happiness
And joy, eating away
At the scrumptious Christmas pudding
And the tweet of a robin
Cold and lonely, going off to sleep.

Reece Murdoch (12)
Prestwick Academy, Prestwick

The Dark

Mornings of gold seem so far away
What has happened to my day?
The sun has fled leaving black and blue
There's not much else to see or do.
But the peaceful sounds of traffic and flights
Could the dark be my light?

The freedom of cover and light of the moon
A luminous beauty can combat the gloom.
Not a glimpse nor a glance can be seen of the dirt
No tensions or pressures of sadness and hurt.
I ask you one question with all my might
Could the dark be my light?

Now my blackness is slowly melting away
I should be glad because here comes the day.
But as the harsh light hits my eyes
I think with a sudden jolt of surprise
Did I really wish away the night?
The dark is my light.

Kelsey Frew (12)
Prestwick Academy, Prestwick

The Joyful Snow

The bare tree stands tall with pride,
On the house the snow blankets the rooftop.
The robin's feathers fire as he sings a joyful tune.
The light gleams through the window
As the flames and smoke run up the chimney.
As the snow floats down from the sky,
The ground layers up and up and up.
The snow reminds me of playing in it with my sniffly red nose.
Hot chocolate is on the top of my mind as it heats up my tummy
And leaves stream dripping from my window.
When I see the white soft snow
It reminds me of cold, white ice cream.
When it's cold and dark in the morning,
It reminds me of waking up on Christmas morning
And decorating the house with the tinsel and the Christmas tree.
On Christmas morning as the snowflakes fall
I hear joyous laughter of children.
Crunch, crunch, crunch, is what I hear
As I walk through the icy snow.
As the fire heats up the house,
Sparks come out the fire and crackle.
The snow on my skin feels like frosty cotton wool.
It's like icy burns when the snowflakes hit my skin.
Happiness hits and when the snowball games start
We are having fun.

Victoria Anne Hendrie (11)
Prestwick Academy, Prestwick

Snowy Winter

As cold wind and snow attacked my face
Like hundreds of little angry ice soldiers
My body was shouting for me to stop
Yet when hope was all but gone I found a glimmer of smoke
As my body filled with hope and my brain forgot about the cold
I almost leaped over the last hill to see my home
Sitting enveloped in snow, proudly at the top of the hill.

As I walked in I saw all of my furniture
Which I see every day, I thought this day was special
As my dying feet got closer to my armchair
I felt a rush that stopped me in my tracks
I fell to the floor and felt surges of pain travelling up my body
I attempted to reach my phone and I missed
And lay there trying to come to terms with my fate.

Blair McGinlay (12)
Prestwick Academy, Prestwick

What Matters To Me?

Friends are what matters to me
Not English, maths or history!
They are around me every day
When I talk with friends I'll be okay.
It is my dearest pleasure, my one and only
Friends are always there to phone me
Whether I'm feeling sad or blue,
Lost and distracted and I don't know what to do.
Talk to my friends day or night,
They have that special something to make me feel alright.

Jonathan Johnston (14)
Rathfriland High School, Rathfriland

What Matters To Me?

What matters to me, is friendship
Friendship isn't just about getting along
It's a lot more than that.
Friendship is when someone is there for you
No matter what
Whether I'm feeling sad or blue
Lost and I don't know what to do
Night or day
I can count on my friends
To make me feel alright
The gossip we talk,
The laughs we share
What matters to me is friendship.

Gemma Truesdale (14)
Rathfriland High School, Rathfriland

My Laptop!

I like it because I can surf online
I like it because it is all mine.
I like it because it sits on my lap,
I like it because I can listen to rap.
I like it because I talk to my friends,
I like it because I can follow the latest trends.
That's why I like my laptop so much,
Life would be strange without it as such.

Katherine Gamble (14)
Rathfriland High School, Rathfriland

What Matters To Me?

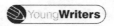

What matters to me are colours,
Colours blue, green and white,
Colours so pretty and precious
Colours so gleaming and bright.

Blue is the colour of calm and cool
Like swimming in a summer pool.
Blue is for the ocean wide
Or those jeans worn with extraordinary pride.

Yellow is for a buttercup,
Also for that balloon that would never blow up.
It is also for the scorching sun
Shining down to give summer fun.

Brown is for the polluted mud
Also for that unpeeled spud.
It is also for my burning toast
Or perhaps that special roast.

Green is for sea-sickened men
Or for my father's most cherished pen.
Green is for the princess' pea
Or for branches on the Christmas tree.

Black is for a music note
Or for the verging extinct black goat.
Black is for death and the night,
Extreme pitch darkness when it's not so bright.

White is for a Westie dog
Or for that agitating morning fog.
White is for a falling flake
And the icing on my fairy cake.

Gold is the trumpet in the band
Or for all those smooth grains of sand.
For that round and extravagant ring
All those bells that go *ding-ding!*

Grey is for those gloomy, dull days
And for all those seagull bays.
Grey is a squirrel from the wood
Also that donkey from your childhood.

Red is for a valentine's heart
For all those who wish never to part.
Red is the colour of a cherry
Or for a ripe luscious strawberry.

Orange is the colour of a basketball
Or the bricks upon my garden wall.
Orange are the leaves before they fall
So many colours before us all.

Life is full of colours,
Millions more than I have named.
Contrasting colours, everlasting colours,
Colours vibrant or pale.

If all was left in black and white,
What a pity that would be.
So I am now so grateful
For that rainbow I can see.

So now when you think of colours
Think of a vast array.
Think of all the beauty
In a wondrous display.

Hannah Skelly (14)
Rathfriland High School, Rathfriland

What Matters To Me

What matters to me is
To make not break
Not fake a mistake
To give not take
To make a cake
Yes, this sounds great
But what am I to fake
And not to take
To cover my mistake
To be what is great
Will never be me
I'm different to you
To me I'm not you
For something so great
That isn't true
Is all just a mistake
That might matter to you.

Gareth McCabe (14)
Rathfriland High School, Rathfriland

What Matters To Me?

Music matters to me,
Especially R 'n' B.
Music can put some in good moods
Or many in bad moods.
Music can be relaxing
Or otherwise distracting.
Music can be used for many occasions
Like winning Olympics and singing national anthems.
Although some people may disagree and throw dramatic tantrums
But either way I'd say music matters to me.

Rebecca Priestley (14)
Rathfriland High School, Rathfriland

What Matters To Me?

A deafening hush as the lights start to dim,
We get to our places as it's time to begin.

The curtains swish back like a red bird rising into flight,
The opening number begins and we sing with all our might.

The nerves are forgotten as we sing and we dance,
In the wings the teachers start to prance.

The show flies by and the interval arrives,
A quick break for all - we're having the time of our lives.

The second half starts with the bad guys on stage
But soon they are caught and in a rage.

The grease paint glistens and shines on our faces,
We dance and sing, keeping up with our paces.

Before we know it the end is here,
I think we all deserve a loud cheer!

Tired and exhausted to home we all head,
The buzz is still with me as I get into bed.

Harry Singer (14)
Rathfriland High School, Rathfriland

What Matters To Me

My imagination
My imagination matters to me for without it
I wouldn't be able to see.
I wouldn't see the world my way
The way I live life every day.
True nature blossoms all around,
Its hidden secrets to be found.
But,
Who knows what fairies, goblins and elves
Are hiding in our wishing wells?
I love all the facts so cool and true
But I love where my mind can lead me to.
The secret doorway, the hidden path,
The talking bear, the laughing giraffe.
All of this within my grasp.
I ask you now, how could I be
If I didn't have these things inside of me?

Susan Hanna (14)
Rathfriland High School, Rathfriland

What Matters To Me!

A farmer by name,
A footballer by game.
I farm on the hill,
On the wing I have skill.
Cows I would prefer,
The teams I like to stir.
Driving in the tractor is class,
I play football on the grass.
I like to farm with my dad,
I like to play rough I may add.

Steven Bready (14)
Rathfriland High School, Rathfriland

What Is Important To Me?

Things that are important to me you say?
Well, I shall tell you and not take all day:
The sunset at dusk and the sunrise at dawn,
The light, white spots on a newborn fawn.
The bright, wide eyes of my curious cat
Who appears to have fallen in love with my hat.
The song of the robin building his nest,
The silence when all in the house are at rest.
The first smile of a young baby relation,
My great-granny's 90th birthday celebration.
The laugh of a friend who's just been ill,
The view of town from my window sill.
An eagle swooping across the sky,
A little chick learning how to fly.
Looking forward when things go wrong,
Listening to the lyrics that are part of a song.
The smile of strangers I do not know
And feeling that I know where to go.
Each member of my family
And of course all those who care for me.
These are things important to me,
Please listen and you might just see
Why they mean to much to me.

Hayley Ferguson (14)
Rathfriland High School, Rathfriland

What Matters To Me

What matters to me is my horse,
She means the world to me.
We've a bond so strong,
The strongest can't break
So watch out for here we come.

We run through the fields,
United as one.
Flying over jumps as we go
Till darkness calls us homeward bound
As the day draws to a close.

As she gazes at me and me back at her
I know what's coming next.
My pockets are emptied,
My sweets are gone
And all's behind the grin.

She's there for me when all goes wrong
And listens to every word.
She's like the BFG
And loves to run free,
It's Flicka who matters to me.

Ashleen Copes (14)
Rathfriland High School, Rathfriland

What Matters To Me?

Swish-swish go the curtains
As I look out to see
My homeland, my country,
That's what matters to me.

I like to be happy,
I like to have fun
With my friends and family
All rolled into one.

My hair must be funky,
All gelled up on top,
With some trendy, cool clothes
That I buy from the shop.

My piano and bagpipes
Are important to me,
Although, like a cat being strangled
Is what some people see!

Some are traditional,
I'm sure you'll agree,
But these are my values
And they all matter to me.

James Frazer (14)
Rathfriland High School, Rathfriland

Fear

As the night fell it was like walking into a dark cave
Searching for a light to guide me through the cold and empty house
Step by step the cold air was piercing my face
There in the distance the glimmer of the moon peeking out
From the clouds shone through the window
From the corner of my eye
I saw a tall dark figure emerging from the basement
My heart was racing, pounding through my chest as I ran upstairs
The figure chasing me in the mirror was . . .

Glen Sheehan (13)
St Joseph's Boys' School, Derry

Malin Head

I will arise and go to Malin Head
Where a caravan awaits me and a stony path will I have.
I will go to the beach and walk along the shore
And still hear it in the deep heart's core.
When I go home I will be sad and sometimes glad
I walked along the shore
And still heard it in the deep heart's core.

Eoin Godfrey (14)
St Joseph's Boys' School, Derry

Spanish Bliss

I drift away on an aeroplane to Spain
As I watch the clouds float and stare to their delight at me.
On the way down to the runaway my ears were popping like champagne bottles.
The Spanish town is Heaven,
Watching the tall structured buildings standing tall - sunbathing.

I run along the shore of the Spanish beaches
Trying my best to avoid those wriggly waves,
Until they catch me and drag me into the beautiful sea.
At night I watch the moon and the stars as they rule the sky.
On the flight home as I am sad to go
I hear the cry of Spain calling me once again.

Scott McAllister (14)
St Joseph's Boys' School, Derry

Trad

I could play trad music all day long.
You can play tunes or sing a song.
When you're sitting down playing a wee tune.
Your mind starts to wander to places like the moon.

There are lots of different instruments in it.
The guitar, banjo, even the drum kit.
You can play jigs, reels, polkas, all tunes
And if you don't play an instrument ah sher bring the spoons.

Mitchel McAteer (13)
St Mark's High School, Warrenpoint

The Seasons!

Spring is here, let's all cheer!
The lambs are jumping
The calves are thumping
The combines are mowing
Spring is here, let's all cheer!

Summer is here, let's all cheer!
Picnics in the sun
Everyone has lots of fun
Splashing in the sea
It's a great place to be
Summer is here, let's all cheer!

Autumn is here, let's all cheer!
It will soon be over for another year
Leaves dancing down the street
Greeting everyone as they meet
Autumn is here, let's all cheer!

Winter is here, let's all cheer!
Jack Frost is somewhere near
Everywhere snowmen appear
The snow falls softly through the night
We can't wait for snowball fights
Winter is here, let's all cheer!

Cara McAvoy (13)
St Mark's High School, Warrenpoint

Laughter

Laughter is the simplest medicine,
When we see a laughing smile
All we can do is laugh back

Laughter is more than just an impulse reaction
Laughter is like a superpower.
When a person is down and in fear,
Laughter can make them full of cheer.

Laughter is one of the only things everybody owns,
If you're white, black, young or old.
If you get laughter in your system,
You'll never feel cold.

When we laugh our stresses float away,
For a time at least they are astray.
If we make others laugh it's like a gift,
It could make them smile or even stop a rift.

So if you think that laughter is needed,
Lay back,
Listen
And let it rip because it's well overdue.

Peárce Branagan
St Mark's High School, Warrenpoint

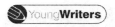

Snowy Weather

It fell from the sky like never before.
It just keeps coming, setting outside my door!

Snow and more snow day after day.
It didn't melt or go slushy.
It wouldn't go away!

It stopped the traffic and the pipes froze.
I didn't have to get up because my school was closed.

Cold white fluffy snow,
It's time to go away.
Okay I might love you,
But I have to get back to school today!

Katie Winters (12)
St Mary's High School, Downpatrick

Little Snowdrops

Here come the little snowdrops pushing through the ground.
Soon they will be tall and straight with white petals all around.
I wish they could stay like that but soon they will be all gone.
Yet next year they will be back again, just as strong!

Catherine Beston (12)
St Mary's High School, Downpatrick

What If?

What if I was never here,
Would everything be crystal clear?
Would anyone notice that I was gone,
Or was I really that boring all along?
I think of all the memories of all my friends,
Will they ever want me back again?
What did I do wrong? I won't do it again.
I just wish this nightmare would really end.

I don't know why this is happening
Or why it's happened to me.
Whatever I did wrong, this isn't the way
It's happened to me.
Whatever I did wrong, this isn't the way
It's supposed to be.
I am really sorry for what I have done
And I wish this could end
And we could go back to having fun.
I've tried my best and that's all I can do,
Well I guess that's the end of us, the end.
We're through!

Meghan Smyth (12)
St Mary's High School, Downpatrick

Our New Arrival

A small pink bundle of joy
Last Friday, was delivered to the Moy.
My auntie and uncle's new baby girl
Had all of us in a swirl.
With a cute button nose, tiny fingers and toes!
Not a sound you would hear from our little Annie-Rose.

Kate McMahon (12)
St Mary's High School, Downpatrick

On My First Day Of High School

On the first day of school,
It was a worry,
I had my big cousin so it wasn't so scary.
I met my principal
And form teacher too,
She took me to class with the girls I knew.
We played a few games to get to know all the names.
We went on a tour just to make sure,
We knew our way to class each day.

Lisa Magennis (12)
St Mary's High School, Downpatrick

There's No Place Like Space!

One day I went to Mars where the stars were shining bright
A Martian came to talk to me.
This gave me a fright!
So I decided to go to Jupiter
I'd heard that it was fun
But a volcano erupted
So I had to run.
I then went to Saturn where I got a burn, so I had to turn
And run to Venus
Again this was a bad idea so I ran to Uranus,
But I shouldn't have gone there.
I decided to go to Pluto but again this was a no no,
So I decided to go to Neptune where I left to go to . . .
Mercury which was actually quite fun
But I missed my home planet and in three, two, one . . .
I was back to Earth.
(I went back on a bus, it's the place for us.)
I will remember my trip to space
Especially Earth because it is ace in space!

Holly Kendall (12)
St Mary's High School, Downpatrick

I Have A Cat

I have a cat
He's black and fat
I think he's really cool!

He sleeps all day
And only plays
When I come home from school!

When I sing he purrs
On my bed he curls
I love my black, fat cat!

Katie Mckinney (12)
St Mary's High School, Downpatrick

First Day At St Mary's

On my first day,
I wished it was May,
Lying in 'til two,
Didn't have much to do.
Now it's big school, the classroom . . . it's so big,
I can't get lost . . . I have mentors . . . right.
Oh, what if I fight with one of my friends
Or I break one of my pens?
Mum said I'd be fine
Now I'm in school and got told my class,
The day went by fast.
I made *new* friends,
I didn't break one of my pens!
Tomorrow will be fun,
My bag will probably weigh a ton.

Chloe Burns (12)
St Mary's High School, Downpatrick

My Dog Fred

I have a dog named Fred
He won't play fetch, he won't play dead
He won't shake hands or sit or stay
Or bark or beg or run and play
He plays with cats instead
I love my little Fred.

Rachel Salmon (12)
St Mary's High School, Downpatrick

Wet Ireland

The sun was like a sauna in the bright sky.
So hot I could not stand it!
What I desired was the ice-cold water of the rain
To fall upon my face
But I could not control the weather!

The thing I will always desire
Is the wet land that I come from.
My priceless emerald isle of sweet Ireland.

Aine Mcstay (12)
St Mary's High School, Downpatrick

My First Day

Here I am standing
Looking at this huge thing.
My heart is thumping
Like a butterfly's wing beat
And I am dressed
In some weird costume.
I see lots of people
Dressed like me!
Finally, a face I know
And that makes me glow inside.

Orla Martin (12)
St Mary's High School, Downpatrick

Our Angel

There's an angel in our house who looks after us.
She's watched over us since we were very small.
She soothes our pains when we are not well.
And if we have problems she's the one we tell.
Our angel loves us when we are good or bad.
When we do well at school she is very glad.
We love our angel, she is our best chum.
She'll guide us through life, she's our loving mum.

Rosemary Wilson (12)
St Mary's High School, Downpatrick

My Pet

My pet is fat and furry!
It rolls around Derry
And when it falls asleep
It dreams of something deep.

When it wakes up each day
It's really, really excited to play!
Its favourite colour is pink,
Milk is its favourite drink.

So that's all about my pet,
You can guess what it is, I bet!

Gemma Tumelty (12)
St Mary's High School, Downpatrick

The Valley

In the lonely evenings,
I like to see the beauty of the valley,
That takes my loneliness away.

The breeze from the valley takes me down to the meadows,
The beautiful singing of the birds,
The valley, the blooming flowers,
All of this makes me feel like flying.

The sun whispers goodbye,
And the stars start twinkling,
Like the dew on the grass.

As the night falls,
I say goodnight to the world,
And remember that wherever I go,
My mind follows.

Diana Varghese (12)
St Mary's High School, Downpatrick

Love And Death

When I say I love you I mean . . .

I want to start each day with you.
I want to finish each night with you.
I want to walk each path hand in hand with you.
I want to grow old with you
Because looking in your eyes shows me my future.
In your arms is Heaven.
I want to share my life with you and end it in your arms.
I want to grow old with you.

Olivia Mooney (12)
St Mary's High School, Downpatrick

My Little Friend

I know you're my little friend
But I hope you're with me right to the end.
You are so special to me,
I don't want to let go.

We share a lot of memories both you and me.
I know all your secrets and you know mine too.
That's what makes me so close to you.
I know you're not happy all the time
But I love you for who you are.
People can hate you but I don't, you're amazing.

I know you have to go
But I will always love you so.

Roisin Rafferty (12)
St Mary's High School, Downpatrick

Wales

W elsh
E isteddfod
L et's
S hout
H ooray

W e
A ll
L eap because
E isteddfod means
S aint David's Day!

Brooke Martinson (13)
St Richard Gwyn Catholic High School, Barry

Cenin Pedr

There they stand, tall and proud,
With their golden mane,
They stand out in the crowd.

Shining there before the rest,
With their heads held high,
They know they're the best.

Higher up in the role they play,
They're just like lions,
Lions of the bouquet.

Lions they are,
Kings maybe,
These kings are part of Wales you see.

In Wales we stand,
Tall and proud,
With daffodils to help us stand out in the crowd.

Jessica Peters (15)
St Richard Gwyn Catholic High School, Barry

John And James

These are my two drops of rain
Waiting on the windowpane
I am waiting here to see
Which the winning one will be.

Both of them have different names
One is John and one is James.

John is moving off at last
James is going pretty fast

John is there and John has won
Look I told you here's the sun!

Jocelin Reji (12)
St Richard Gwyn Catholic High School, Barry

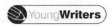

Chasing Waves

It was a bitter but sunny morning
I went for a surf
The water was freezing
But I could take it.

The waves were coming in
In sets with a big period
It was a perfect offshore wind.

I sprinted down to the beach
Put my leash on
Had just jumped over the waves.

I got out to the back door
Waited for the right wave.

It came
It was perfect
It was the best wave I ever had
I nearly got barrelled
I did a big bottom turn
And *bang!* I fell!

Emily Gillard (13)
St Richard Gwyn Catholic High School, Barry

Over The Bar

The wind in my hair,
The silent breezy air,
I cannot forget this moment in time,
Keeping me alive,
Your bouncy hair,
You really don't care,
Just keep running far and far,
It's you and me, over the bar . . .

High in the sky,
We can almost fly,
Further and further,
We're almost there,
Over the rainbow,
Let people stare,
'Cause it's just you and me,
We just don't care.

Even if you don't have a friend,
Something that doesn't speak can almost make amends,
You're not alone
No time to mourn,
Every day, just do what you do
And you'll be okay.

Emily Ward (14)
St Richard Gwyn Catholic High School, Barry

Have Pride In Your Nation

Have pride in your nation for we are Wales,
There's more to our people than downing the ales,
With the Red Dragon so bold, so brave,
We take the pride of our nation to our grave,
With our daffodils so beautiful, so gold,
And our St David the stories we're told,
With our sheep in the fields who graze all day,
And our delicious leeks how they cook them that way,
With Cardiff the capital of our nation,
And our own language so full of sophistication,
With the north and the south and the east and the west,
As we unite we become the best,
And our people with Wales running through their blood so red,
If you think you're not Welsh, it's just in your head,
Wales the mythical land of Arthur and Gweneviere,
Where songs like Cŵm Rhondda and Calon Lan can be sung with a tear,
Green fields all around,
Yet our miners worked deep underground,
In search of the coal,
Also known as Wales' black gold
With our Millennium Stadium standing so proud,
And when the rugby's on you should see the crowd,
As we sing 'Mae Hen Wlad Fy Nhadau'
With all our pride,
The other team looks at us as they cower and hide,
As the dragon on the flag dances gracefully in the breeze,
The other team just stand there as they shake at their knees,
The beauty of rugby as we fly down that pitch,
As the other team defends us with a slight hitch,
With tears of an adult and the cheers of a child,
We run across the line and the crowd goes wild,
At the end of the game with a triumphant defeat,
The other team walk past as they stare at their feet,
They shout, 'You were lucky!' but they shout it with irony,
We roar back, 'We *are* lucky, for we are Wales, *we are Cymru!*'

Jade Saif (12)
St Richard Gwyn Catholic High School, Barry

Broken Love

My body is aching,
My heart is breaking,
I can't deal with the pain,
It's as endless as the rain.

I need you to help me,
To set my heart free,
So the pain will end,
And my heart can mend.

What is our love,
Is it as pure as a dove,
Or as cold as ice,
And controlled by a dice.

Maybe my feelings have changed,
My mind rearranged,
My heart's now a maze,
As clear as a cloudy haze.

I'm not sure what to think,
My mind is on the brink,
To save me from the fall,
All you have to do is call.

Just tell me that you love me,
And we can then finally be,
Happy at last,
And forget the past.

Charlotte Edmunds-Jones (14)
St Richard Gwyn Catholic High School, Barry

Colours

(Inspired by 'The Sound Collector' by Roger McGough)

Darkness is coming near,
It seems to be closing in,
I feel like something's missing,
It's a fight I cannot win.

The colours all disappear,
And everything's a blur.
My life feels very empty,
Oh, I wish there was a cure.

The cars as they go by,
They leave a sound behind.
Yet nothing I can see,
Oh, I wish I could rewind.

The colour of the sky,
The greenness of the trees.
The colours of the rainbow,
And the stripes upon the bees.

The crowded city streets,
The memories flooding back.
I can't see anything,
Apart from the colour black.

The brightness of the sun,
The stars in the night.
Life was so wonderful,
I loved that pretty sight.

Everything was clear,
Until the darkness came.
He took everything away from me.
Now life will never be the same.

Celyn Campbell & Leah Howells (11)
St Richard Gwyn Catholic High School, Barry

A Recipe For A Welsh Myth

Sprinkle in a dark windy night!
With one special star standing out
A horse with special armour
A rich king that can also shout.

A dollop of a shining ring
That everyone would want
A special scroll for the king
With Roman italic font.

Chuck in a poor little victim
That is threatened to be kicked out of town
Mix in an evil witch
Make sure you melt her down.

Dash in a red Welsh dragon
That is alive to protect a sword
Mixed in a locked up princess
Don't forget the boastful lord.

Pour in some deathly poison
Make sure you don't swig some
Rip in a royal invitation
Leave out 'You're welcome to come!'

So after all that, you've nearly done
Make sure you haven't caught a disease
Slap in the brave hero
But don't forget his return bus fees.

Alysha Harrison (12)
St Richard Gwyn Catholic High School, Barry

A Recipe For A Welsh Myth

Begin with a castle high up on a mountain,
Then add some coins in an old-fashioned fountain.
Stir in some pheasants that are hungry and cold,
Chuck in some bones that are rotten and old.
Mix in some failure, but mostly success,
Chop up a damsel in distress.
A dash of bravery
And a hint of slavery.
A sprinkle of skill,
A bucketful of thrill.
A handful of snakes,
An ounce of mistakes.
A teaspoon of mystery and an old, ugly troll,
Pour in some blood with a small, tattered scroll.
Add two swords in a stone and a pure gold ring,
An evil, ugly and ungrateful king.
Add ten truckloads of dragons that are weird and strange,
Then a twist, like the prince being rescued for a change!

Jade Clarke (12)
St Richard Gwyn Catholic High School, Barry

My Comfort Zone

My comfort zone is . . .
Where I can listen to my favourite tone,
My comfort zone is in front of the TV drinking a mug of tea,
And my comfort zone is fresh and warm,
My comfort zone is just right,
Not on a stressful aeroplane,
Or a scary fright,
My comfort zone is loving and caring,
My comfort zone is our family home.

Nicole McGarrigle (12)
Sanquhar Academy, Broomfield

The Velociraptor

Nine-year-old girl playing outside
In the long grass,
Next to her house
Running about noisily.

A loud scattering sound
At the other side,
Catches her attention
And she gallops over.

She tries to shout
But as she tries
It is too late,
The last thing she sees
Is a sharp claw in her face.

Nobody knows what had happened
Until the next day . . .
A summer's morning 100 million years ago.

Michael Anderson (12)
Sanquhar Academy, Broomfield

Buzzard

Missing the mouse by a fraction,
The buzzard is back and ready for action.
As the mouse runs for shelter,
Twisting and turning, the bird hits it a pelter.

The buzzard had won, the rodent had lost,
That poor creature lying dead in the frost.
The fearless bird was standing so happy,
He made a loud noise and was named Big Yappy.

Grant Hannah (12)
Sanquhar Academy, Broomfield

The Salmon

The salmon is beautiful
It swims the Nith
Trying to get home
What a hard life a salmon has.

It leaps, jumps and spurts up the falls
It's trial and error
Oh how I would love to catch her
She's a beauty
I want her for my tea.

She's pink and silver with brown dots
She's round about fifty-two pounds
When I see her my mouth waters
Imagining how she would look on my plate.

Ryan McCron (12)
Sanquhar Academy, Broomfield

I Know A Dog

I know a dog called Raffy
And he is a Staffy
He is brown and white
And not very light.

I feed him Pedigree
But his belly does not agree
Raffy likes playing with balls
When he jumps to get them he just falls.

He is my favourite Staffy
And his name is Raffy.

Paul Sanderson (12)
Sanquhar Academy, Broomfield

The Boxer

Standing at the ringside
Nervous as could be
Was the boxer
Waiting for round three.

As the bell rang aloud
The boxer was so proud
He had won the fight
With a mighty strike.

He held his hands up with might
And was ready for his final fight.

Kieran O'Connor (12)
Sanquhar Academy, Broomfield

The Cat

He blinks upon the rug
He yawns and rolls around
The fire's heat so warm and cosy
The cat lies there and does the roly-poly
The fire dims out and the cat tires out.

The next morning he starts warming
As the sun beams through the window.

Murray McColm (12)
Sanquhar Academy, Broomfield

The Magic Box

(Based on 'Magic Box' by Kit Wright)

I will put into the box . . .
The coliseum with its grey bricks
Animals of the rainforest
Italian food fit for a Roman emperor

I will put in the box . . .
The squelching of the mud of the rainforest
A vial of the River Nile
A stone off Mount Everest's highest peak

I will put in the box . . .
The rain of the Australian flood
The bark of the last magic tree
The whole of the Red Sea in a bag

I will put in the box . . .
The sun and the wind of the great Sahara Desert
The red of the fire round the sun
The blue of the oceans covering Planet Earth

My box will be made of fire, rock and gold
It will stay under my bed
And it will also hold the great living sphinx.

Thomas Bell (12)
Sanquhar Academy, Broomfield

Ma Dug

Ma dug is running faster
Than she's ever ran before
In a supersonic circle
In the middle of the floor.

Aaron Baillie (13)
Sanquhar Academy, Broomfield

Smiler

I have a dog called Smiler
He is a rottweiler
He likes Pedigree Denta Stix
He is black with a hint of brown.

My dog is overweight
I think I feed him too much
But I suppose it shows I love him
He is really special to me.

Smiler likes playing football
He always bursts my footballs
But I suppose he loves me
I am really special to Smiler.

Ross Cook (12)
Sanquhar Academy, Broomfield

Haiku For Teegan

Teegan is drawing.
Concentrating very hard.
Back straight, drawing dreams.

Megan Cameron (14)
Stobhill School, Glasgow

I Just Want The Old Me Back

Desperate to be back
To normal
She cries out
In pain
Why must it be?
She tries
And tries
But one way or
Another
She always
Ends up feeling worse
She doesn't want
To eat
It makes her want
To cry
She gets
Voices in her head
'You wanna look like me'
'You're fat'
'Nobody likes you'
She cries even
Louder
And all she
Wants
Is to be her
Old self again
But she can't
She's falling
Deeper and deeper
But what she doesn't know
She's a strong, strong person
She's just got to believe it.

Roxanne Rae (17)
Stobhill School, Glasgow

For Evermore

The fear inside is growing
Far from here the death bell's tolling
The waters of the night are flowing
And the nightingale is crowing
The darkness shades the burning light
And in the corner of my room
Where sunlight faded first to gloom
An angel comes to sight
I feel the burning of its eyes
I hear its wild unearthly cries
I turn my head in shame and fear
And so I see the angel's tears
Fall grey upon the floor
And the world was night for evermore.

Emma Warnock (15)
Stobhill School, Glasgow

Colin

Y ou bore me with your work. You go
O n and on and on
U ntil I'm
R eally bored
E very day

A ll you talk about is
W hiffy cheese and milk
E verywhere I look you're
S tanding with the biology book. It goes in
O ne ear and out the other, it hurts
M y mind
E very class I'm in is one too many.

Kayleigh McGregor (14)
Stobhill School, Glasgow

Blades

When you look
At its smooth, shiny texture
And you feel
Its smooth run
It feels
Scary but warm.

You get shivers
As you grasp it
You feel
The adrenaline
In your body
And you hold your breath.

It feels weak
But powerful
You feel hurt
But healed
That is the damage
A single blade
Leaves behind.

Nicole Alexander (13)
Stobhill School, Glasgow

Perfect

Why
Can't I
Be perfect?
Be a bird on the wing
A song of a king
A flower blossoming true
Why can't you
Think I'm perfect?
If just one
Person believed in me
I would believe in me too.

A sharp sweet shock
A hasty retreat
From my taste of victory
Taste of madness
For that is where perfection lies
Beyond the hills littered with those
Who were almost there
It's not fair,
That we should be treated this way.

Our hubris, reaching, reaching for the sky
Punished so harshly,
We are undone, unloved, unscrewed
From our sockets
And sent to the lonely, distant moon
Because we reached for the stars.

Julia Mark (15)
Stobhill School, Glasgow

Chocolates And Sweets Are Delicious Treats

Chocolates and sweets are delicious treats
But warning, be careful how many you eat!
There's white, milk and dark chocolate to choose.
They melt in your mouth and quickly go away,
But you would definitely wish they'd stay another day.
Just remember to brush your teeth right away,
Or else, they will rot away, as quickly as the chocolate stays.
'I think we should have a change,' the pallet would say.
Chocolates and delicious treats but what about sweets?
Chocolates and sweets are the most delicious treats,
But sweets are the most ambitious treats.
Why ambitious, the sweet tooth would say?
I think it's the flavour they have to crave.
The sweet and the sour flavours are luxurious I must say.
I love chocolates,
I love sweets,
Best of all I love them as treats,
My heart will keep them for whatever reason,
Forever and ever and ever,
No matter what occasion.
Chocolates and sweets are definitely my delicious treats.
But if your heart desires something different,
And your taste buds are saying it too,
Don't hesitate, just try something new.

Taiba Hussain (11)
Taibah School, Cardiff

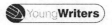

My Parents

My parents to me are so dear
When they're by me there's no fear
All the love they give me
All the time they spare for me
They do this because they love me dearly
And would never think of leaving me.

When I am feeling upset my parents will hug me
At this they're simply the best
When there's a tear in my eye
My dad will ask, 'Why?'
When I explain, he'll understand
And never lets go of my hand.

My mum cooks amazing food
She's always in a good mood
My mum is my mother, sister and my friend
If I carry on, this poem will never end!

Suhaima Khan (11)
Taibah School, Cardiff

My Mum

My mum is the most important person in my life.
I'm so grateful for my mum because without her I wouldn't be here.
You will never find a mum like mine because she is one of a kind.
My mum is as bright as the sun and as sweet as honey.
She helps me with all my problems, no matter how big or small.
She is always there to catch me when I fall.

Tamanna Khan (12)
Taibah School, Cardiff

Dear Dad

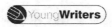

There's a special kind of feeling when I think about you, Dad.
It's a pleasure to remember all the amazing times we've had together.
There's a special kind of caring that is meant for you alone.
And there's also a very important place in my heart
That only you can fill, Dad!

Khadija Abdirizak (12)
Taibah School, Cardiff

Decisions . . . Decisions . . .

So many paths, don't know which one to take,
Laid out in front of me, continuing on.
Only one path is right, the other two are fake.
Another choice yet to be made which will lead me on,

To be right or wrong it is not certain.
The path on my right leads into a wood;
The dangers are hiding behind a curtain,
And the path on my left, well I would,

But it's covered with brambles, thorns and hurtful things.
Last of all is the path in the middle;
A clear path with flowers, a bird just sings.
I have made up my mind it's the middle.

It's vital I make the right choice,
For the outcome will depend on the choice I make.
Never follow others, follow your own voice.
Hopefully the consequence will be something you're happy to take.

I hope this won't be a choice I'll come to hate,
But now I'd better hurry, it's getting late!

Hera Siddique (15)
Taibah School, Cardiff

Friendship Matters

Friendship is a magical power
Overtaking every evil!

Forever friends can last,
Always smiling as they go past,
Hand in hand they walk,
Laughing as they talk,
Never saying mean words,
Sweetly talking like birds.

Friendship is something you can never break,
Like roses on a thorn bush you can never take,
A strong friendship fires away the evil,
A strong friendship keeps you happy.

Friendship helps you get through life,
Friendship is important.

If you don't have a strong friendship
Your smile will fade away.

Amarah Siddique (12)
Taibah School, Cardiff

What Matters To Me

What matters to me is my little brother,
I love him because he is family,
He is nothing like my mother,
He sometimes can be lovely.

What matters to me is my little brother,
He is a little devil,
I would not want another,
He is as tough as a pebble.

Michaela Harris (11)
Ysgol Gyfun Gwynllyw, Pontypool

What Matters To Me?

What matters to me is rugby.
I love it because it makes me feel free.
I also like it because you can play rugby.
Once I was playing and I hurt my knee.

What matters to me is rugby.
The team I play for is St Joseph's, we play in yellow.
I make all the boys cry, 'Mummy!'
When the ref comes over we say, 'Hello.'

Jamie Mirfin (12)
Ysgol Gyfun Gwynllyw, Pontypool

What Matters To Me

What matters to me are my pets
I love them because they're funny
And I am sad when they go to the vet's
But they cost a lot of money.

My dog is what matters to me the most
I love him because he's cute
Every morning he steals my toast
I go to school hungry, what a brute!

Rhys O'Brien (12)
Ysgol Gyfun Gwynllyw, Pontypool

What Matters To Me Are Friends

What matters to me are friends
Sometimes they drive me around the bend
I'll still stay with them to the end.

Friends make me feel alive
Friends, friends, lots of friends
I still can't get over they broke my dad's drive
But I would never kick them out of my little hive.

Joel Harley Edwards (12)
Ysgol Gyfun Gwynllyw, Pontypool

What Matters To Me

What matters to me is rugby
I love it because it's fun
And because it's lovely
I love it when it is in the sun.

What matters to me is rugby
I love it because I love running
And because it makes me feel happy
I feel excited when I'm kicking.

Jack Jones (11)
Ysgol Gyfun Gwynllyw, Pontypool

What Matters To Me

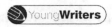

What matters to me is compassion
I love it because it makes me feel warm
It's never out of fashion
It's better than being in a storm.

I like compassion because it's polite
Without compassion I will be torn
Compassion shows people to be nice
Selfishness makes me feel forlorn.

Olivia Barnby Davies (11)
Ysgol Gyfun Gwynllyw, Pontypool

Untitled

What matters to me is running
I like it because I enjoy sport
I never stop loving it
It's better than doing nothing.

Running is important to me
Because it makes me feel proud
I always run
So it won't let me down.

Courtney Jones (12)
Ysgol Gyfun Gwynllyw, Pontypool

What Matters To Me

What matters to me is football
I love it because it makes me feel excited
I could hear the crowd roar
My favourite team is United.

What matters to me is my dog
I love him because he's cute
He chases logs
My dog is as long as a flute.

What matters to me is my iPod
I play games all the time
I ride on my quad
This is how I rhyme.

Alexander Harrison (12)
Ysgol Gyfun Gwynllyw, Pontypool

A Long Way To Rathtool

The line on our map takes a dip
As we go on a very long trip.
We look at the map
And pass our first lap.
Up and down, left and right;
We hoped we didn't lose the light
'Cause it's a long way to Rathtool
And we might have to refuel.
We might end up travelling at night,
But the map is usually right.
Expressways, motorways, two lanes,
Dirt tracks and an odyssey across the plains.
Rathtool awaits us at dawn,
And we will soon pass lawn after lawn.
We stop at a gas station
In this oh-so-big nation
And get snacks and drinks cheap
So thoughts of hunger can't reap.
We fill the car up to the brim
But not so the fuel overflows the rim.
We get ready for the last leg to our destination
But hope that we shan't stop at another station.
Rathtool bustles during day, and relaxes at night
But let us hope our instincts about the place are right.
We roll along the road steadily
But not so that we speed manically.
Nearly there now, my friend,
But how much have we to spend?
Rathtool comes into sight at last.
And now we start to approach the place, fast . . .

Matthew Wilson (17)
Ysgol Plas Brondyffryn, Denbigh

My Sister

To me you are an angel in disguise,
Full of intuition, intelligent and wise.
Always giving and helping through
Good times and bad.
You are the best friend I've ever had!
If I had one wish it would surely be
To give you as much as you've given me.
Though I've put our relationship
Through some cloudy days,
You've been my sunshine in so many ways.
You gave me your hand whenever you could.
Thank you so much, my sister, my friend,
My gratitude for you has no end.

Hannah Holland (13)
Ysgol-Y-Gwendraeth, Llanelli

Football

F un in the area
O utstanding cheers
O wning players on the other teams
T umbling across the pitch
B ouncing the ball across the pitch
A round the stadium shouting
L oving the match and the scores
L iving the dream by watching the game.

Connah Bevan
Ysgol-Y-Gwendraeth, Llanelli

Pepi

Day by day I miss your smell,
The times we walked around the park.

The way you slept with your paws in the air,
The times you only let me brush your hair.

How eager you were to get in the car,
You're now looking down at me from a star.

You were the best I ever had,
I always love and always have.

Every night there is a candle upon your grave,
To symbolise that to see you, is what I crave.

I miss you day and night,
You weren't the type to bite.

You always were my boy,
The only feeling that I had with you was joy.

You looked up at me with shining eyes,
Now I'm looking up at you in the clear blue skies.

I spent 15 years, 1 month and 16 days with you,
I can assure you that time flew.

Why do the best ones go first?
I don't think I can feel any worse.

You were my best friend,
I wish this poem could never end,
But my love will never, my friend.

Christian Evans
Ysgol-Y-Gwendraeth, Llanelli

Wales Vs England

Rugby, rugby, on TV
Sit back and relax, let's see.
All around balls are thrown,
Catching, caught, kicked and blown.

Try, try, what a score,
Don't stop Wales, we want more.
England, England, go back home
See that thing, it's called a phone.
Go back now, no red blood flown.
Oh if you stay, punches would be thrown.

In the end, Wales will win,
Easy boys, heads in bins.
Chants and cheers from the crowd,
Sweet, sweet song, with beautiful sound.

At 10 o'clock, on the dot
Pubs and bars, drinks held high.
Men and women will forever remember that day
When Wales beat England!

Robert Lewis
Ysgol-Y-Gwendraeth, Llanelli

Horse Riding, My Favourite Hobby

Thumps and bumps on the way to the country park
Heart racing with excitement who's there before me
I squeal, stop the car, had enough of this lark
Run to book my ride, had to go, bang my knee

Wait with anticipation while girls take their turn
Patience is now wearing thin
Rubbing it hard to stop the burn
It's all right, only scuffed the skin

Groom and pamper until he's ready
Saddle, bridle and the rug
Whoa boy, keep it steady
Bridle in hand with a big tug

Hear him breathing, stomping, chewing
Boot in stirrup, whip in hand
Off he goes chomping and rearing
Hooves thumping in the sand

Feeling the wind in my face
Down sandy trails we go
Nothing around but empty space
Ducking under branches that're low

Horseshoes leaving their print
Thumping a tune with a beating heart
We take the straight at a sprint
A powerful four legged dart

Shining, glistening, what a treasure
Sun shines on him like a halo
Sixteen hands at last measure
My gorgeous golden palomino.

Deanna Griffiths
Ysgol-Y-Gwendraeth, Llanelli

Don't Do Dangerous Drugs

Taking pills could make you ill
How I wonder what it would be like six feet under
Smoking weed could stop you doing a good deed
The need to want more and more could stop you thinking no more
Taking speed could make you ill
Even though it takes you far over the hill!
Doing aerosols could make you hallucinate
It even makes you hate your best mate
Taking coke could make you choke
Even though it numbs the pain, don't take cocaine

Even though these drugs get you high
There's a possibility that you could die.

Brandon Hulme
Ysgol-Y-Gwendraeth, Llanelli

Rugby

R ugby is repetitive
U nsupported you will get tackled
G rab the ball and score
B *ang*, you're down on the floor
Y ou might have broken your leg.

Craig Davies
Ysgol-Y-Gwendraeth, Llanelli

Rugby

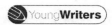

R unning through the mud as fast as the rain,
U nexpectedly fall over the damp pitch,
G entle but lots of it, the time ticks on,
B all crosses their try line,
Y ells from the crowd as the ref blows up for full-time.
We win.

Ronan Lewis
Ysgol-Y-Gwendraeth, Llanelli

Alcoholic

She sits there with no money
And can't feed her children
But somehow she still
Finds the money to get that alcoholic drink!

I don't find it good
The way that she might be,
The way that she sits there and drinks her life away.

Her children are not even able to talk
But they use their little bodies to survive
The only food they get is in the microwave from yesterday.

If those children survive they will be amazing
And they will shine
They will know their way to live life.

I don't find it good the way she drinks
Her life down the drain
Just because of that alcoholic drink!

Zoe Thomas (14)
Ysgol-Y-Gwendraeth, Llanelli

My Dad

I'm glad you're my dad
You really are the best
You're smart and strong
Kind and blessed
You make me laugh
You make me cry
But most of all
You make me smile
Whenever I'm down
You're always around
To keep me safe and sound.

Andrew Harrison (13)
Ysgol-Y-Gwendraeth, Llanelli

What Matters To Me

Rugby matters to me,
The thrill of being on the field,
The feeling of hope when you're winning,
The rewarding cheer when the ball lands on the other team's try line,
The silence when the kicker kicks the ball over the posts
And the scream from the crowd when he succeeds,
The relief when the whistle blows,
The feeling that I helped the team reach its goal,
This is what matters to me.

Adam Stallard (12)
Ysgol-Y-Gwendraeth, Llanelli

My Little Brother

My little brother
All he ever does is whine and (cone) all day
But in his cuteness lies a little monster in wait.
Once let loose he'll cause havoc
Hitting, kicking, scratching and even biting!

Annoying me all day everywhere we go
There's a problem, I can't run away.
My mum and dad say I have to do this and do that with him all day.
Give him a bowl of sugar or a load of sweets
And you'll regret it for the rest of the day.

He zooms around the place like the world is going to end.
Shouting in your ears until they ring like bells.
The only thing is that he can't help it.
Sometimes I wonder where he gets it.
I wonder if it's me!

Kallum Stone (13)
Ysgol-Y-Gwendraeth, Llanelli

What Is Music?

What can be said about music?
Music can mean so much to the listener.
It can lift your mood
And take you away through the years,
Back to a memory you'll cherish forever.
But it can also make you remember the sad times,
The times when you turned to music for comfort and support.
A certain song at a certain time can last forever.
Then when you hear that song you smile or sigh
With the memory of the time you listened to that particular tune.
So ask yourself, what can be said about music?
And think of a time music has inspired and comforted you.

Emily Cartwright (12)
Ysgol-Y-Gwendraeth, Llanelli

The Poem That Matters

The music I like is a little bit different
The music I like is not a favourite to every soul in the planet
But it is to a few
The music I like will or won't be for you
The music I like is heavy as a boulder
The music I like, the music I like . . .

Michael Winter (12)
Ysgol-Y-Gwendraeth, Llanelli

My Pets

Noise, noise everywhere, barks, quacks, grunts and squeaks,
A black shaggy blur bolts across the kitchen, it's Ebony my Tibetan terrier,
A *cheep-cheep* in the dining room, two yellow birds flapping their wings, it's the canaries.
A *splash-splash* as fast as a bolt of lightning, it's the fish.
A *chomp-chomp* in the living room, *bang-bang* on the vivarium, it's the tortoise.
A *grunt-grunt* a fluff ball waddles across the living room floor, it's Sindy the Pekingese puppy,
A chewing and scratching all night long, I can rely on them to keep me awake, it's my chinchillas,
A *cock-a-doodle-do, cock-a-doodle-do,* what's that? Of course, it's the cockerel . . .
These are my pets.

Tiwdwr Glover (12)
Ysgol-Y-Gwendraeth, Llanelli

My English Poem

There are loads of different sports
In a pool or on a court
Running or swimming
Team games for winning
Tennis or basketball
Any type for you all

Football's my main one
We don't score none
But we keep our heads high
And look at the sky, and say
Tomorrow we'll win and they will pay

Skateboarding is great
But that's the one I hate
I have a go
Fall on the floor
Or even through someone's door.

Rachel McLoughlin
Ysgol-Y-Gwendraeth, Llanelli

Motocross Life

Every life has a starting gate.

Everyone is just waiting for that 30 second board to go down
and for the gate to drop, hoping that we get the whole shot.

We have our rhythm sections, that are pretty tough to go through,
and sometimes we just pass them by.

We have our ups and downs, such as the uphill and downhill jumps.

Sometimes you crash and don't get up, but you must try to get up
and recover the race.

In this race you're always trying to beat everyone
and trying to get to the top, and when the time comes,
and you do things right, you win!

And when you don't win, sometimes you just have to start another race,
maybe rebuild your bike better or have a better strategy to win.

Your pit crew and the people around you trying to support you
and take care of you, but sometimes you have to take matters into your own
hands, and do it for yourself.

But when it comes down to the end, it's how you finish, how much effort you
put in to it, how much time you're willing to go through, how badly you want
it all.

Kofi Stimpson-Williams
Ysgol-Y-Gwendraeth, Llanelli

Untitled

I don't really know why people are afraid of the night,
You can't see anything at night, because it's dark.

During the day you have to walk past
Hundreds of blank faces,
People who have hurt you,
People who have changed you,
People who have changed for you
And people who have betrayed you.

You can't see any of this
When it's dark outside,
So what need is there to run and hide?

But really, isn't that what we fear the most?
Not being able to see anything?

How confusing are we.

Kelly Phillips
Ysgol-Y-Gwendraeth, Llanelli

What Matters To Me

What matters to me,
Is my 'Call of Duty'
And I am a beauty.
I quickly scope your face
And you're a disgrace,
You can't kill
'Cause it's in your will.

What matters to me
Is my Xbox 360.
I would play on my bed,
Until I am dead.
They tell me to drop
'Cause I make their ears pop.

Dean Harries (11)
Ysgol-Y-Gwendraeth, Llanelli

What Matters To Me

I'd rather get an education
Than sit around and play PlayStation.
I'd really rather go to school
Than mope around playing pool.

There's so many opportunities out there
That most people would stop and stare.
It's not all computer games and TV,
There's CVs, jobs and university!

People used to laugh at me,
When I said, 'I want a degree.'
But what they don't realise
Is there's jobs of all shapes and size.

Don't you get it,
Can't you see
My education matters to me!

Indeg Crane (11)
Ysgol-Y-Gwendraeth, Llanelli

What Matters To Me

What matters to me
Are sharks in the sea,
A big blue fin
The rest in the bin.

Makos are fast
But are also vast,
Whale sharks are big
And tigers eat like pigs.

Goblins have long snouts
Secured I have doubts,
Cookie cutters are odd
And are often caught by a rod.

Mathew Davies (12)
Ysgol-Y-Gwendraeth, Llanelli

What Matters To Me

I like sports, especially these two
Rugby and football I like the best
They both have balls that bounce really high
Although with the football I kick to the sky.

They both go on for ages
Rugby lasts for eighty minutes
Football for ten more
So when I've finished I like to sit and draw.

The pitch is always muddy
I always find the wet patch
Even when it's dry
Especially when I've scored a goal or a try.

Daniel Conibeer (12)
Ysgol-Y-Gwendraeth, Llanelli

What Matters To Me

Rugby is my life
I'm a rugby maniac
My brother plays as well
Scarlets, Welsh squad, also Pontyberem
We both play for Pontyberem
I'm a flanker, he's a prop.

I play in mud and snow as well
As you probably know
I support Scarlets
I know that they're the best
I don't support the rest
Like Ospreys
They always get crushed by Scarlets' under sixteens.

Rhys Evans
Ysgol-Y-Gwendraeth, Llanelli

Mum's Sunday Lunch

What matters to me . . .
The smell is out of this world,
The mashed potato is soft like candyfloss,
Her carrots are beautifully cut,
The chicken is narrow and tasty,
The gravy is dense and delicious,
We all eat at the dining table
Together as a family.
Now that is what I call
A brilliant meal!

Rhys Davies (11)
Ysgol-Y-Gwendraeth, Llanelli

What Matters To Me

What matters to me is my family
We like to play about
That's no doubt
I love them dearly

We all like having takeaways
All week long
On the dining room table
Listening to our favourite song

We all like all kinds of sports
But in our hearts we like watching rugby
As we watch players have a sin bin
We all hope Wales will *win!*

Cerian Evans
Ysgol-Y-Gwendraeth, Llanelli

What Matters To Me

Rugby is what matters to me,
The sport is rough and dirty,
It includes rucks, scrums and kicking,
It also includes tackling,
We play in the mud, snow, whatever the weather.

I play on the wing,
Because I'm fast and skilful,
I catch the ball and run to the try line,
Before we play a game,
We have to train.

Rugby is all about teamwork
And communicating with others,
It's not all about you,
It is a team sport,
Rugby is what matters to me.

Josh Hopkins (11)
Ysgol-Y-Gwendraeth, Llanelli

What Matters To Me!

Rugby matters to me,
My family loves rugby,
I play for the district
Scarlet East.

I have training Monday
Six till seven in the night,
My position is centre.

Steffan Owen Jones
Ysgol-Y-Gwendraeth, Llanelli

What Matters To Me

What matters to me,
Are my lizards Jacko and Lizzy.
And not forgetting Morgana,
Whose patterns are like a banana.
Lizzy the lizard,
Is a Blazing Blizzard.
And the gecko called Jacko,
Once walked on tobacco.
Morgana's so cool,
I once took her to school.
One day they're fat,
They're nocturnal like a bat.
One day they're thin,
Once every month they all shed their skin.
The short term for leopard gecko is Leo
And I like to call them the Leo trio!

Austin Hooper (12)
Ysgol-Y-Gwendraeth, Llanelli

What Matters To Me?

Gwen is my dog,
She likes chasing cats,
She can be as soppy as a baby
And was bred to kill rats.

Mum makes all the beds,
Mum does all the shopping,
Mum does all the cooking,
We think it's really boring.

Dad goes out to work,
He likes fixing cars,
My mum calls him the dishwasher
And she says he comes from Mars.

Louise Mead (11)
Ysgol-Y-Gwendraeth, Llanelli

What Matters To Me

What matters to me,
Is a trip to the sea,
With all my precious pets,
Our fishing rods and nets,
With all my friends and family.

What matters to me,
Is my extended family,
There's my younger sister Ellie
And my older cousin Kelly,
They're all so lovely.

What matters to me,
Is my pet dog Bailie,
She's fluffy and cute
And brown like a leather boot,
That's everything you see!

Drew Orchard
Ysgol-Y-Gwendraeth, Llanelli

What Matters To Me

I love beds, they are very comfy.
You can watch TV and eat food on it.

I love my family, we're very close
Except for the ones that live in England,
TV and PlayStation are lush
But there's a lot more stuff.

I love my dogs
They're very special in my life
So is my cat, her name is Tammy.

My hobbies are rugby,
My favourite team is Ospreys.
My favourite international team is England,
At the moment they're second in the Six Nations.
They're going to thrash Italy.
My other hobbies include PlayStation.
My favourite game is 'Call of Duty Black Ops'.

Cameron Smith-King
Ysgol-Y-Gwendraeth, Llanelli

What Matters To Me

What matters to me
Is Meg.
Can't you see?
She's the dog
That everyone loves.

She's very fast
She'll never be last
I love her
And she loves me.

All night, all day
She guards with no pay
Waiting on the window sill
Guarding us.

Super hearing and super scents
Using it with a bunch of sense
She can also
Run a marathon.

Colours all round
White, black and brown
You can't take
Her colours away.

You can say
She likes to play
With her toy
A ball on a rope.

Ryan Walters (12)
Ysgol-Y-Gwendraeth, Llanelli

What Matters To Me

My family matters to me,
If I need them they will be there
And I never forget to look after my family when they need me.

When I grow up
I will try my best to make them happy,
I will try to help them if I can,
The only thing I can say,
That I love them
And I know they love me too.

I get them presents,
They get me presents,
I'm thankful
I've got them for my family.

Sam Cavill
Ysgol-Y-Gwendraeth, Llanelli

Guitar

G uitar is what matters to me
U can learn how to play it,
I t is the best thing I've got,
T o play all night,
A bass is nice,
R ock bass guitars are my favourite guitar.

Randell Denning (12)
Ysgol-Y-Gwendraeth, Llanelli

Me And My Cousins!

My cousins mean a lot to me
They always end up making me laugh
But last weekend we went out for food
And we didn't talk that much to each other.

But we did enjoy our day out being together
But we hardly get to see each other
They live in Amannford and I live in Tumble
So I was glad to see them that weekend.

And we all had a slice of birthday cake
Which was my aunt's birthday at the same time
That's why we all went out for a meal
And we all enjoyed.

But the funniest girl there was Ellie because she read a poem out
About her grandmother and she made us all laugh
And it took us all a long time to stop.
But inside the poem it had her grandmother's best friend inside
Because they always go on holiday together
And sometimes when they go on holidays there's something going on!

Nia Davies
Ysgol-Y-Gwendraeth, Llanelli

What Matters To Me

My motorbike is everything to me
It is fast, it is orange and black
And it means the world to me
I could ride it all day and night through the sunlight
I'll never get enough of my motorbike
My motorbike is everything to me.

Jake Thomas
Ysgol-Y-Gwendraeth, Llanelli

My Dog!

My dog matters to me with her cute little floppy ears flopping everywhere.
Running round the garden 100 miles per hour.
We play catch, we're running out of breath.
Gemini is my friend.
We call her Gem for short.
She is so cute like a little teddy bear.
She likes to lie on my feet at night, nice and warm.
She sometimes goes to sleep on my head at night.
She is full of joy, gives me hugs and kisses.
We play all day having fun so I say.
I love her so much.
She never barks and never growls.
I love her so much.
She means the whole world to me
You see.

Kathleen Harris
Ysgol-Y-Gwendraeth, Llanelli

What Matters To Me?

My family matters to me, we always have fun playing games
Sometimes we will go for a walk down by the beach
Or we will have a treat by going to the cinema and watching a film
But what is more important is spending time with them while I can.

When I was really bad they were there for me
They would do what they could to help me
So I am going to try to make up to them by helping them
So I am very thankful for what they did for me.

Sasha Smith (12)
Ysgol-Y-Gwendraeth, Llanelli

Love Is

Love is sweet and so are you.
Keep me close and we'll be true.
Love is patient and forgiving,
Always constant and forever willing.

Love fills your heart with joy,
Kisses flow when girl meets boy.
Love is faithful, love is blind,
Always caring, forever kind.
Love is a ring that binds us together.
Love never dies, and lives on forever.

Mari Llewelyn (13)
Ysgol-Y-Preseli, Heol Hermon

Love

Love is a cool winter breeze,
Love makes you fall to your knees.

Love is the smell of a red rose,
Love makes me lift right off my toes.

Love makes you feel sky high,
Love also can make you cry.

Love can be the green apple on the tree,
But after all this you still don't love me.

Ashley Farmer (14)
Ysgol-Y-Preseli, Heol Hermon

Love Is

Love is as sweet as a Haribo ring,
Love is as colourful as roses,
Love is as hot as a summer's day,
Love is . . .

You're my vegetable in my soup,
You're my orange in Terry's Chocolate Orange,
You're my stubbornness in the bull,
Love is . . .

You're like a ray of sunshine,
You bring light and happiness in,
My life would be so much darker if you had not come in,
Love is . . .

Roses are red,
Violets are blue,
The sun will shine
All over you,
Love is . . .

Llyr Edwards (13)
Ysgol-Y-Preseli, Heol Hermon

I Love You

I love you with all my heart,
It makes me feel whole, when I think you are mine.
When I first saw you,
You stood out from the crowd,
Like the sun suddenly shining on you, only you.
When I am close to you, you smell as sweet as spring.
When I hear you talk, it's like you're singing a beautiful song.
I will care for you, cook for you, make you feel loved.
That is how much I love you.
I will keep you warm in the winter,
Make you feel safe when you're scared.
I will love you for evermore.
I will love you for eternity.
I love you.

Holly Thackray (14)
Ysgol-Y-Preseli, Heol Hermon

The Lament Of The Princess Bride

My lover, clad in black night,
Four ships faster than the wind,
I have sent for you, to light the path home.
Love of this kind occurs rarely if ever,
But as the sea claims the ships,
Love is stolen from us, forever,
White dress, and another's lips,
I am their victim at dawn,
Haunted by things that could have been,
I wait for your love, forlorn,
But if church bells chime, I am Queen,
But there is a chance, hope is ours,
We may bloom like autumn flowers.

Dark like ebony death, my love we die,
Two rotten hearts enveloped in cotton,
We beat close, yet so far apart we lie,
Deep in the graveyard of love, forgotten,
I'll weep in my wedding bed, cut my hair,
Away with the autumn locks you once kissed,
Out to the high seas I'll call in despair,
To the wind alone my love shall be hissed.
But where sails the ship with my black knight?
My love on a slave ship, fly my freedom, come!
Is the love that he holds for me burning bright?
Is the work of the years already done?
But our souls are never truly apart,
And regal title will never claim my heart.

Danielle Tose (15)
Ysgol-Y-Preseli, Heol Hermon

YoungWriters

Featured Poets:
DEAD POETS
AKA Mark Grist & MC Mixy

Mark Grist and MC Mixy joined forces to become the 'Dead Poets' in 2008.

Since then Mark and Mixy have been challenging the preconceptions of poetry and hip hop across the country. As 'Dead Poets', they have performed in venues ranging from nightclubs to secondary schools; from festivals to formal dinners. They've appeared on Radio 6 Live with Steve Merchant, they've been on a national tour with Phrased and Confused and debuted their show at the 2010 Edinburgh Fringe, which was a huge success.

Both Mark and Mixy work on solo projects as well as working together as the 'Dead Poets'. Both have been Peterborough's Poet Laureate, with Mixy holding the title for 2010.

The 'Dead Poets' are available for workshops in your school as well as other events. Visit www.deadpoetry.co.uk for further information and to contact the guys!

Read on to pick up some fab writing tips!

Your WORKSHOPS

In these workshops we are going to look at writing styles and examine some literary techniques that the 'dead poets' use. Grab a pen, and let's go!

Rhythm Workshop

Rhythm in writing is like the beat in music. Rhythm is when certain words are produced more forcefully than others, and may be held for longer duration. The repetition of a pattern is what produces a 'rhythmic effect'. The word rhythm comes from the Greek meaning of 'measured motion'.

Count the number of syllables in your name. Then count the number of syllables in the following line, which you write in your notepad: 'My horse, my horse, will not eat grass'.

Now, highlight the longer sounding syllables and then the shorter sounding syllables in a different colour.

Di dum, di dum, di dum, di dum is a good way of summing this up.

You should then try to write your own lines that match this rhythm. You have one minute to see how many you can write!

Examples include:
'My cheese smells bad because it's hot'
and
'I do not like to write in rhyme'.

For your poem, why don't you try to play with the rhythm? Use only longer beats or shorter beats? Create your own beat and write your lines to this?

Did you know ... ?

Did you know that paper was invented in China around 105AD by Ts'ai Lun. The first English paper mill didn't open until 1590 and was in Dartford.

Rhyme Workshop

Start off with the phrase 'I'd rather be silver than gold' in your notepad. and see if you can come up with lines that rhyme with it -
'I'd rather have hair than be bald'
'I'd rather be young than be old'
'I'd rather be hot than cold'
'I'd rather be bought than sold'

Also, pick one of these words and see how many rhymes you can find:

Rose

Wall

Warm

Danger

What kinds of rhymes did you come up with? Are there differences in rhymes? Do some words rhyme more cleanly than others? Which do you prefer and why?

Onomatopoeia Workshop

Divide a sheet of A4 paper into 8 squares.

You then have thirty seconds to draw/write what could make the following sounds:

Splash	Ping
Drip	Bang
Rip	Croak
Crack	Splash

Now try writing your own ideas of onomatopoeia. Why might a writer include onomatopoeia in their writing?

Lists Workshop

Game - you (and you can ask your friends or family too) to write as many reasons as possible for the following topics:

Annoying things about siblings

The worst pets ever

The most disgusting ingredients for a soup you can think of

Why not try writing a poem with the same first 2, 3 or 4 words?

I am ...

Or

I love it when ...

Eg:

I am a brother

I am a listener

I am a collector of secrets

I am a messer of bedrooms.

Repetition Workshop

Come up with a list of words/ phrases, aim for at least 5. You now must include one of these words in your piece at least 6 times. You aren't allowed to place these words/ phrases at the beginning of any of the lines.

Suggested words/phrases:

Why

Freedom

Laughing

That was the best day ever

I can't find the door

I'm in trouble again

The best

Workshop POETRY 101

Below is a poem written especially for Poetry Matters, by MC Mixy.
Why not try and write some more poems of your own?

What is Matter?

© MC Mixy

What matters to me may not be the same things that matter to you
You may not agree with my opinion mentality or attitude
The order in which I line up my priorities to move
Choose to include my view and do what I do due to my mood
And state of mind
I make the time to place the lines on stacks of paper and binds
Concentrate on my artwork hard I can't just pass and scrape behind
Always keep close mates of mine that make things right
And even those who can't … just cos I love the way they can try
What matters to me is doing things the right way
It's tough this game of life we play what we think might stray from what others might say
In this world of individuality we all wanna bring originality
Live life and drift through casually but the vicious reality is
Creativity is unique
Opinions will always differ but if you figure you know the truth, speak
So many things matter to me depending on how tragically deep you wanna go
I know I need to defy gravity on this balance beam
As I laugh and breathe draft and read map the scene practise piece smash the beat and graphic release
Visual and vocal it's a standard procedure
Have to believe and don't bite the hand when it feeds ya

If you wanna be a leader you need to stay out of the pen where the sheep are
The things that matter to me are
My art and my friends
That will stay from the start to the end
People will do things you find hard to amend
Expect the attacks and prepare you gotta be smart to defend
I put my whole heart in the blend the mass is halved yet again
I'm marked by my pen a big fish fighting sharks of men
In a small pond
Dodging harpoons and nets hooks and predators tryna dismember ya
I won't let them I won't get disheartened I can fend for myself
As long as I'm doing what's important
I'm my mind where I'm supported is a just cause to be supporting
In these appalling hard times I often find myself falling when
Only two aspects of my life keep me sane and allow me to stand tall again
Out of all of them two is a small number
It's a reminder I remind ya to hold necessity and let luxury fall under
Try to avoid letting depression seep through
Take the lesson we actually need a lot less than we think we do
So what matters to you?
They may be similar to things that matter to me
I'm actually lacking the need of things I feel would help me to succeed
Though I like to keep it simple, I wanna love, I wanna breed
I'm one of many individuals in this world where importance fluctuates and varies
Things that matter will come and go
But the ones that stay for long enough must be worth keeping close
If you're not sure now don't watch it you'll know when you need to know
Me, I think I know now ... yet I feel and fear I don't.

Turn overleaf for a poem by Mark Grist
and some fantastic hints and tips!

Workshop POETRY 101

What Tie Should I Wear Today?

© Mark Grist

I wish I had a tie that was suave and silk and slick,
One with flair, that's debonair and would enchant with just one flick,
Yeah, I'd like that … a tie that's hypnotizing,
I'd be very restrained and avoid womanising,
But all the lady teachers would still say 'Mr Grist your tie's so charming!'
As I cruise into their classrooms with it striking and disarming.
At parents' evenings my tie's charm would suffice,
In getting mums to whisper as they leave 'Your English teacher seems nice!'

Or maybe an evil-looking tie - one that's the business,
Where students will go 'Watch out! Mr Grist is
on the prowl with that evil tie.'
The one that cornered Josh and then ripped out his eye.
Yeah no one ever whispers, no one ever sniggers,
Or my tie would rear up and you'd wet your knickers.
Maybe one girl just hasn't heard the warning,
Cos she overslept and turned up late to school that morning,
And so I'd catch her in my lesson yawning … oh dear.
I'd try to calm it down, but this tie's got bad ideas.
It'd size the girl up and then just as she fears,
Dive in like a serpent snapping at her ears.
There'd be a scream, some blood and lots and lots of tears,
And she wouldn't be able to yawn again for years.

Or maybe … a tie that everyone agrees is mighty fine
And people travel from miles around to gawp at the design
I'd like that … a tie that pushes the boundaries of tieware right up to the limit
It'd make emos wipe their tears away while chavs say 'It's wicked innit?'
and footy lads would stop me with 'I'd wear that if I ever won the cup.'
And I'd walk through Peterborough to slapped backs, high fives, thumbs up
While monosyllabic teenagers would just stand there going 'Yup.'

I don't know. I'd never be sure which of the three to try
As any decision between them would always end a tie.